D1553895

# How to Use
# AF & RF
# Signal Generators

**DEDICATION**
To Sylvia, for more reasons than can be named.

———————————————————

**Other TAB books by the author:**

Book No. 921    The ABC Book of Hi.Fi/Audio Projects

No. 927
$8.95

# How to Use
# AF & RF
# Signal Generators

By George deLucenay Leon

TAB BOOKS
Blue Ridge Summit, Pa. 17214

FIRST EDITION

FIRST PRINTING—OCTOBER 1977

Copyright © 1977 by TAB BOOKS

Printed in the United States
of America

Library of Congress Cataloging in Publication Data

Leon, George, 1914-
   How to Use AF & RF Signal Generators.

   Includes inex.
   1.Signal generators. 2.Electronics Apparatus&
Appliances--Testing.  I.  Title.
TK78727.S5L46     621.3815'48     77-15127
ISBN 0-8306-7927-8
ISBN 0-8306-6927-2 pbk.

# Foreword

A signal generator is commonly thought of as an instrument for signal tracing. While that is one of its important functions, it is a far more versatile tool. In the hands of the knowledgeable technician or hobbyist it becomes an extremely versatile instrument. The many uses listed in this book will provide you with a good, solid foundation for your future work with signal generators. For there are many more uses that have been and will be discovered by imaginative workers in the field of electronics. Examples of the art of signal generator use presented in this book illustrate particular facets of the instrument and should serve to stir the mind of the reader to find other uses.

Signal generators range from the simplest tone producers to those which, in the hands of the informed user, will make testing faster, easier and above all, more dependable. If it is useful to most technicians, it is of inestimable value to the circuit designer at all levels. Naturally, the better the instrument, the more functions it offers...and the more expensive it is apt to be.

It is sometimes true that all one needs is a single-tone generator which is employed to follow a circuit through its maze of wires; but even then, if the instrument varies in its output, it can deceive the user. Therefore, it should always be remembered that the signal generator with an attenuator circuit is a source of variable AC voltage.

It is an advantage, of course, that a generator's output signal voltage is available at varying frequencies. This feature allows measurements otherwise impossible with a fixed frequency, voltage variable transformer.

The signal generator is not a difficult instrument to understand, and with this book we will explore its many uses to make it the most valuable test instrument on the bench!

In this book I have endeavored to include a cross-section of a variety of generators. My purpose is to enable one to become at ease with this large family of test equipment by building some of the units shown in these pages. Also included are specifications and capabilities of a variety of manufactured generators. This list although by no means complete, should make future choices of purchase easier.

George Leon

# Contents

# Acknowledgments

Many manufacturers have been extremely helpful with suggestions and technical data. Special thanks are due to the following companies who furnished photographs and technical data on specific models of their generators: Eico (Electronic Instrument Co.), Heath Company, Hewlett Packard, Hickok Electronic Instrument Co., Marconi Instruments, Photolume Corp., Tektronix Inc., and Wavetek.

Thanks are also due to Leslie Solomon, Technical Editor of *Popular Electronics,* for his suggestions on the subject of the use of triangle waves for testing.

# Chapter 1
# The Signal Generator

A signal generator *belongs* on every workbench. A hobbyist or technician needs a signal generator in one form or another just as much as the bread-boarding engineer. While it is readily understood by everyone that the engineer who designs, builds and troubleshoots complicated equipment has at least one generator in front of him, it is not so well accepted that the "Sunday kit-builder", or the hobbyist who puts a simple electronic unit together, also needs a generator. If for no other reason, he can use it as a signal checker to reassure himself that even as seemingly insignificant an item as a solder joint is holding fast. It is true that his needs will differ from those of the engineer. Since the engineer requires a generator just as sophisticated as the equipment he is checking, obviously the kit-builder needs something a good deal simpler. However, in these days when the average hobbyist/technician is putting together involved amplifiers, preamps, TV sets and home computers, the days of the moistened finger for checking stage gains are long past.

Our average electronic worker may have a variety of equipment to enable him to develop and carry out tests. These will certainly include an oscilloscope, a multimeter, a capacitor checker, a resistor substitution box and lots more, depending on the type of work he is involved with. The multimeter may be digital instead of the more common analog, or it may be specialized such as an audio VTVM, and the scope may offer dual trace and trigger sweeps, but he will *always* have a signal generator. While the beginner has often learned (to his misfortune) that a circuit usually needs troubleshooting before it will work as it should, it comes as a shock (albeit a gratifying one) to discover that even the design engineer may spend a great portion of his time in attempting to improve his circuit. It, too, rarely works just as it theoretically did on paper or on the breadboard the first time around. Although the scope will show a trace, the engineer can only find what is wrong, what causes the distortion and how much of it there is, with the aid of the signal generator. He knows that, without some version of this important instrument, a link in the test chain is missing. For example, the scope cannot be used to its fullest if there is no signal generator to originate a tone of known frequency and amplitude. If the engineer (as well as the hobbyist) doesn't know what goes in, how can he judge the quality of what comes out?

The type generator used may vary from the simplest single-tone oscillator to check continuity, to the ultra-sophisticated generator boasting outputs of dual or even triple waveforms, with log and linear sweeps; it may have a frequency range from 1 Hz all the way up to several hundred megahertz. This brings up the question: How complicated a generator does one need?

Basically, it depends on two factors...the knowledge possessed by the user and the complexity of the equipment being checked. Since the beginner electronic hobbyist is not apt to choose a complicated circuit to build, he can limit himself to a relatively simple generator. As he becomes more proficient and develops his skills, he will naturally escalate to better testing facilities. His needs will increase proportionately with his abilities. He will demand a generator able to offer him more controls, greater ease of operation, as well as greater dependability and repeatability. To operate the complex generators, more knowledge is required than is generally possessed by the tyro. It would be foolish to complicate one's life by having a unit that one cannot handle and it is even more foolish to buy or build a generator that one will have "outgrown" in a short time.

The importance and necessity of a signal generator on all workbenches was graphically illustrated in a recent query of engineers, technicians and hobbyists. To the question, "If you could have only three test instruments on your workbench, which would they be?" In most cases the answer was, "An oscilloscope, a multimeter and a signal generator." To narrow the choice further, the next question was: "If you had a choice of two, which would they be?" The answer was, "A signal generator and an oscilloscope." (The oscilloscope can fulfill some functions of the multimeter as it can directly measure voltages and indirectly, current and resistance.)

The generator takes guessing out of testing. With an accurately calibrated scope and generator, you can obtain precise measurements indicating the actual condition of the particular circuit, complete unit, or even the individual component under test. Every pertinent parameter of a circuit can be ascertained with the aid of the signal generator.

It should not be overlooked that a signal generator is not only a source of one or many frequencies, but is also a source of *controlled* and measured AC voltage. This latter function permits the testing and matching of a variety of components by applying a voltage, not only variable as to amplitude, but also of frequency.

Many components will either not react to the line frequency of 60 Hz or the test at that frequency will be inadequate, requiring the ability to go up the scale to find at what point, for example, a transistor ceases to be of value. This particular function of a signal generator should always be remembered.

## JUST WHAT IS A SIGNAL GENERATOR?

According to the John Markus *Electronics and Nuceleonics Dictionary,* a signal generator is defined as a "test instrument that can be set to generate an unmodulated or tone-modulated RF signal voltage at a known frequency..." On the other hand, in Heath's manual, *How to Understand and Use Your Signal Generator,* that instrument is described as one that "produces electrical oscillations." The John Marcus dictionary goes on to state that "there are two main categories of signal generators, AF and RF generators. An oscillator is a circuit that generates alternating current at a frequency determined by the value of its components." This can be summed up by saying that a signal generator is a signal simulator, whether RF or AF, and that term oscillator is sued interchangeably in the general literature.

In this book, to avoid any possible confusion, the term *oscillator* is used to describe an oscillating circuit. The signal generator, for our purpose, is an instrument which contains an oscillating circuit plus a variety of other circuits to control amplitude and/or frequency and measure output voltage. While it is true that signal generators usually refer to RF units, we will consider that a signal generator may range from the bottom of the audio range—40 Hz—up through the radio frequencies into the megahertz region. So, our signal generators will be either AF or RF, and in some cases both ranges are built into one unit.

A typical signal generator consists of four basic parts: an oscillator circuit, capable of producing one or more frequencies; an amplifying stage to boost the signal from the oscillator; a power supply to feed both the oscillator and amplifier stages; and an attenuator circuit to reduce the output signal to match the needs of the unit under test. Some signal generators will also have an impedence matching circuit to enable the generator to equalize its output to that of the following unit. Without that feature, the generator cannot be used for accurate measurements, although it does not preclude its employment as a signal simulator when all that is needed is a relatively distortionless wave of a given frequency and amplitude. Figure 1-1 shows a typical signal generator in block form.

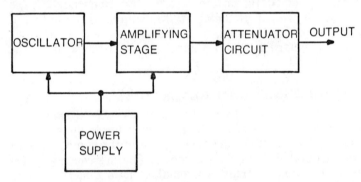

Fig. 1-1. Typical signal generator block diagram.

To explain the action of an oscillator is to think of a stone being thrown into a pond. This causes the waves, as they spread out, to become weaker and eventually die away. But what the oscillator is, in effect, is to imagine a second stone being thrown into the pond just after the first one. As the waves from the first stone reach the edges of the pond they bounce back and meet the second set of waves. This causes an interaction between the two sets of waves with one wave reinforcing the other. As more stones continue to be dropped, the waves continue this interaction building up until they begin their own set of secondary waves getting bigger and bigger. This, of course is a simplified explanation. In the signal generator the electrical impulses, like our imaginary stones, continue the interaction. To understand the workings of the generator, let us take a typical two-transistor circuit as shown in Fig. 1-2.

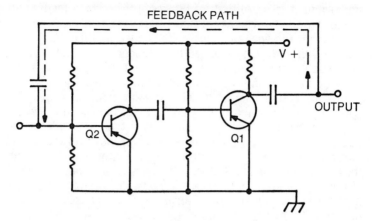

Fig. 1-2. Two-transistor oscillator.

A small signal is amplified by the action of transistor Q1. At the same time, the signal undergoes inversion. The part of the cycle which increased before the first stage will be decreased by the action of Q1; that part of the cycle which decreased before amplification is now increased. This reversed and amplified signal goes through the coupling capacitor to the second transistor Q2. The same inversion process occurs so that the double inversion now restores the cycles to their original form. They are now in phase with the original signal. Naturally, further amplification has occured. Several transistors can be strung together for additional amplification and inversion at each stage. The greater the signal is at the input, the greater it will be at the output—until a point is reached where the transistors are over-driven and the amplification is distorted or the transistors are ruined. The output signal is in phase with the input for every *even* number of stages.

In an amplifier the worst thing that can happen is oscillation. Design engineers do all in their power to prevent this. But, what is unacceptable in an amplifier is just what is wanted in an oscillator. To accomplish this effect, we convert the amplifier to an oscillator by feeding a part of the output signal back to the input. Since the output signal is now in phase with the input, due to the double inversion, we have a positive (or regenerative) feedback. Note the dotted line in Fig. 1-2. This is the feedback path causing the amplifier to go into oscillation.

The action can be compared to someone speaking into a microphone in a room where a loudspeaker connected to the amplifier is nearby. The microphone picks up the original signal and it is amplified by the amplifier, which feeds that signal into the loudspeaker. But, the microphone picks up the sound from the speaker and sends it back into the amplifier. The action will continue getting louder and louder until oscillation occurs. It is heard as a squeal or a howl and is the same action as in the typical oscillator.

In an actual oscillator, no external signal needs to be applied. Oscillation merely requires turning on the switch which controls the voltage supply. This type of oscillation is caused by a difference in starting times between two alternating waves. See Fig. 1-3. The oscillator output, seen at the collector of the transistor, is fed back to the input by means of the capacitor-resistor network connected between the base and the collector of the transistor. This causes a phase difference between the input and the output starting times, resulting in oscillation.

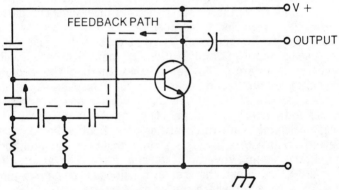

Fig. 1-3. One-transistor oscillator.

Transistors were used in the above examples since their ancillary circuitry is simpler than those of tubes. Tubes require two voltages for their operation, although the principle is the same; the action of the transistor is more easily explained, only one voltage being used. Then too, the transistorized generators have an advantage in that they can be used independent of power lines. Batteries are eminently suitable for this operation. Voltages with the transistorized equipment will range from five to eighteen volts at 10 to 20 mA.

Tubes are by no means to be considered obsolete and some of the finest of present day equipment is still tube driven. They naturally require a 115-volt AC line for power and need several minutes to stabilize the tubes before they can be employed, as compared with the instant-on capability of transistors. But, greater overall stability has been claimed for the tubes.

Needless to say, integrated circuits (ICs) have crept into the act and several generators use such "op amps" for their oscillation producing device. In Fig. 1-4, a one-IC signal generator is diagrammed and which can be easily built in an hour.

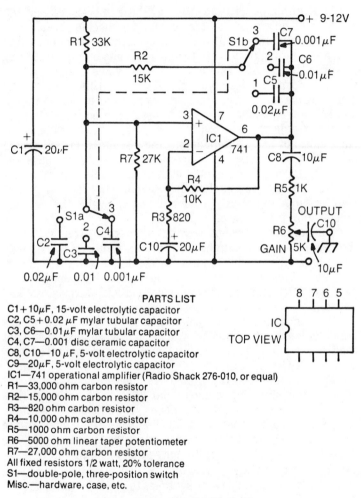

PARTS LIST

C1+10μF, 15-volt electrolytic capacitor
C2, C5+0.02 μF mylar tubular capacitor
C3, C6—0.01μF mylar tubular capacitor
C4, C7—0.001 disc ceramic capacitor
C8, C10—10 μF, 5-volt electrolytic capacitor
C9—20μF, 5-volt electrolytic capacitor
IC1—741 operational amplifier (Radio Shack 276-010, or equal)
R1—33,000 ohm carbon resistor
R2—15,000 ohm carbon resistor
R3—820 ohm carbon resistor
R4—10,000 ohm carbon resistor
R5—1000 ohm carbon resistor
R6—5000 ohm linear taper potentiometer
R7—27,000 ohm carbon resistor
All fixed resistors 1/2 watt, 20% tolerance
S1—double-pole, three-position switch
Misc.—hardware, case, etc.

Fig. 1-4. Single IC audio generator.

The numerous resistors, capacitors and transistors all internally mounted on one IC chip offer excellent stability characteristics to the designer. Apart from this inherent stability (due to the fact that any changes of temperature will be equally absorbed by all of the internal components) is the plus in that the one chip takes up less space than a tube socket. The IC signal generators are usually battery powered and the whole unit can be dropped into a technician's tube caddy and be "lost." The bulk of the unit is made up of the various switches and controls which have to be kept large enough to be easily handled.

The simple generators, such as those in Figs. 1-2 and 1-3, can be used only as signal tracers and for checking breaks in a circuit. Such a unit will oscillate at only one frequency and with a waveform that is apt to leave much to be desired. While it is true that signal tracing requires only one frequency, and the waveform is unimportant, there are times where the generator must be able to offer two, three or an unlimited number of frequencies with an almost distortion-free output.

By adding a switch, several resistor-capacitor combinations are switched into the oscillator circuit. Each position of the switch produces one frequency. While some generators use one capacitor with various values of resistors (each ten times greater than the previous one) the converse is also employed, the capacitors changing while the resistor value remains the same.

Such an arrangement permits only as many frequencies as there are switch positions. While it is limiting, there is an advantage in that the pointer on the knob of the frequency control indicates fairly accurately the frequency being generated by that particular combination of resistors and capacitors.

A method used to obtain continuously variable frequencies is to include a potentiometer which, in a sense, does just what the fixed resistors in a switching arrangement do: introduce a different R-C combination.

Specific ranges are obtained in some generators by means of a switch selecting a particular R-C combination with a variable capacitor to achieve continuously variable frequencies within that band. Eico's Model 379, a sine/square wave generator, uses a variable capacitor to determine the basic frequency with a multiplier switch to obtain multiples of $\times$ 10, $\times$ 100, $\times$ 1K, $\times$ 10K and $\times$ 100K. On the other hand, the Eico Model 378 uses only switches to produce the frequency desired. Heath's sine wave generator Model IG-72 employs three detent switches to obtain the cycles in units, tens and the multiplier switch which is marked $\times$ 1, $\times$ 10, $\times$ 100 and $\times$ 1000. These models, as well as others illustrated, employ a far more complex circuitry to produce exact and repeatable settings with dependable output stability over all of their ranges than do the simple examples of oscillators discussed earlier. These circuits, as they stand, would suffer from varying output levels and inconsistent frequencies. However, we now have several circuits (which have become standard in the industry) to overcome these problems.

Needless to say, actual signal generator circuits are far more complex than would be imagined from some of the previous simple circuits shown. One of the most widely used circuits, to achieve amplitude stability of the test signal, is the Wien Bridge. This bridge, as shown in Fig. 1-5, is made up of R1 R2, R3, R4, C1 and C2. A wide range of frequencies are generated by varying C1 and C2 or R1 and R2. The difference in this type of oscillator is that although the feedback path goes through the bridge as in our previous example of a typical oscillator, here there is both a regenerative, (or positive feed back as in Fig. 1-2) and a degenerative (or negative) feedback path. As you will note in Fig. 1-5, the negative feedback occurs at the junction of R1 and R2 and is fed to the emitter of Q1. This increases the reverse bias to the transistor and as a result, less current flows through Q1. The regenerative or positive feedback path goes through R4, C2, C1 and R3 to the base of Q1. This positive feedback is greater than the negative and oscillation occurs, however—at only one frequency, which is determined by the time-constant circuit composed of the four R-C components listed above.

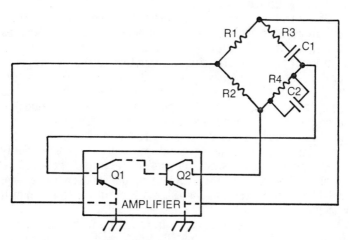

Fig. 1-5. Wien bridge oscillator.

At that frequency, the output and input signals are starting at the same time and are therefore, as the engineers state it "in phase". This in-phase state causes oscillation. At other frequencies, the negative feedback signal cancels the positive and no oscillation can occur. It is because of this dependable action (oscillations occuring at only one frequency), that the Wien bridge oscillator is such a popular circuit.

As the circuit stands, with those components listed, the oscillator would be a single-tone generator. Obviously, this would limit its use. However, by either switching in different values for some of those four components, or by making one or two of them variable, we can obtain a broad range of frequencies. This brings us one step closer to what the signal generator should be capable of.

While all four components can be varied to obtain unlimited frequencies, it is simpler to first begin by making C1 equal C2 and R3 equal to R4. Then, we can use the following equation:

$$F \text{ (frequency)} = \frac{1}{2 \, (R4 \times C2) \, 3.1415}$$

In the bridge circuit, R1 and R2 provide amplitude stability (height) of the waveform. To meet the terms of our equation, we can vary R4 and C2 or just one of the two. While some signal generators offer continuously variable frequencies by means of a variable capacitor, others may employ a series of switched values for the components that make up the time constant.

There is, however, one problem in the theoretically perfect generator described. A resistor changes value as it becomes hot, i.e., a resistor's value will shift up and down depending on the amount of current flowing through the resistor at any given moment. The more current, the hotter becomes the resistor. But the equation remains true only as long as R2 retains its initial value. Due to current flow, R2 will change in value and our equation is no longer accurate. To solve this problem, one can use temperature-compensating resistors which are used in many circuits. A simpler solution, and one considerably cheaper, is to place a small incandescent lamp in the resistive leg of the bridge circuit. This principle is used in several models of both Heath and Eico signal generators. Here's how it works:

As the oscillations increase in the circuit, the lamp heats up and the heating of the filament results in increased resistance. But, the increased resistance creates more degenerative (cancelling) feedback. As this increases, the oscillations are reduced. As they decrease, the lamp becomes cooler and thus its resistance is reduced. This allows the oscillations to become greater. This fluctuation happens at such a rate of change that the oscillations are maintained at a seemingly constant level.

Earlier, when we used the analogy of dropping stones into a pond to create continuous waves, or oscillations, we stressed the fact that if the stones were not continually dropped, the waves would soon dissipate until the pond was smooth again. In our oscillator, instead of stones we employ a small electrical push to give added impetus to the oscillations to prevent them from dying out.

There is still another method of producing oscillations. This is by means of the Hartley oscillator. The circuit is shown in Fig. 1-6, which should be studied during the explanation that follows. This is a vacuum-tube oscillator in which a coil is connected between grid and anode of the tube. This coil is made up of two parts: the tuned coil proper, and a small "tickler" coil. The tap, which connects the two sections of the coil, is in turn connected to the cathode at cathode potential and feedback path is thus created between grid and cathode. Current flowing through the "tickler" coil makes it act like the primary of a transformer and induces voltage flow in the upper or larger coil. This behaves as positive feedback, placing a plus voltage on the grid of the tube. This causes more current to flow through the tube and the associated tickler coil, repeating the previous action until the tube is saturated and no further increases can occur. C2 is part of the grid bias filter and C3 is a bypass capacitor.

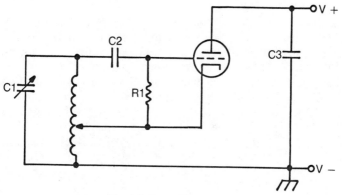

Fig. 1-6. Hartley oscillator.

The amplitude is constant, due to the rapid ups and downs of the current flow. Frequency is primarily dependent on the size of the coil and secondly by the variable capacitor, C1.

It can be seen that the actions of the two oscillators are not so different. In one, a coil is substituted for the filament of the lamp, but the basic principle remains the same.

Still another popular circuit for producing oscillations is the Colpitts circuit. It uses a coil and two capacitors and so is called an L-C circuit. See Fig. 1-7. This type of circuit offers a fairly wide range of frequencies with good waveforms. The parallel-tuned tank circuit consists of two capacitors in series with a common connection at the cathode. Again, it should be remembered that it is unimportant whether it is a tube in the circuit or some solid state component. In the circuit shown in Fig. 1-7, C1 and C2 act as voltage dividers with the coil, L1, in parallel.

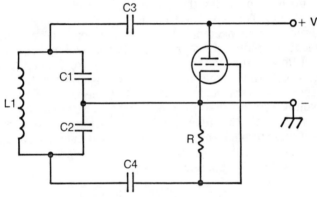

Fig. 1-7. Colpitts oscillator.

Our theoretically perfect signal generator produces pure tones only; that is, there are no harmonics present with the fundamental tone. If the waveform is perfect, there is no apparent distortion, and since harmonics create distortion, then we can say that the perfect sine wave has no harmonics. Harmonics are described as a multiple of the fundamental frequency. On the piano, if middle C is struck, the first harmonic will be a tone one octave above it. But as we said, our sine wave, if it is distortionless, has no harmonics. To obtain harmonics, we want to generate more complex waveforms, which is the subject of the next section.

## WAVEFORMS

Three waveforms are in common use and one or all three may be used for testing equipment. This is not to mean that other, more complex waveforms are not encountered in electronics. Television particularly, as well as FM in the mono, stereo, and quadruplex modes, have many waveforms (which we will not discuss here to avoid unnecessary complications, as well as baffling the hobbyist who is intent in learning the fundamentals of waveform theory).

The three waveforms in general use are sine, square and triangle waves. The others are more specialized and we would recommend the texts available devoted to that particular subject. Of the three mentioned above, each has a reason for being employed for testing. Sine and triangle waves are used in both RF and AF ranges; the square wave, less so, for the reasons which will be mentioned at length in the section on that waveform. Figure 1-8 shows the shapes of the three common waveforms. It should not be forgotten that even if they seem to bear no resemblance to each other, they may have the same frequency and the same amplitude.

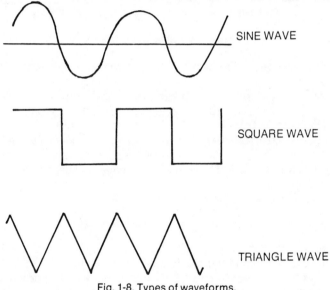

SINE WAVE

SQUARE WAVE

TRIANGLE WAVE

Fig. 1-8. Types of waveforms.

## Sine Waves

Sine waves may be considered as the old standby. This type of wave is defined as one with an amplitude varying as the sine of a linear function of time. See Fig. 1-9. That is the official definition, but for our purposes we will regard the sine wave as one that is relatively simple to create. A 115-volt AC line produces a sine wave at precisely 60 Hz. Although line voltage varies during periods of heavy use, its frequency does not. This can be easily seen by placing the probes of an oscilloscope (very carefully) into a wall outlet. A perfect sine wave will be apparent (set the sweep selector of the scope on the 10 to 100 Hz range). If it were not for the stability of the frequency, electric clocks would be far less accurate than they are.

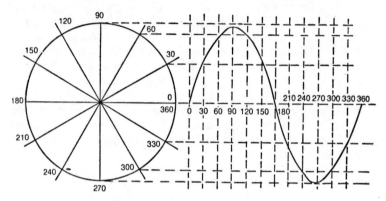

Fig. 1-9. Derivation of a sine wave.

To produce a sine wave, a simple two-transistor generator is shown in Fig. 1-10. This type of circuit is known as a cross-coupled multivibrator circuit. To reduce it to its basics, the explanation for its behavior can be put very simply by saying that as transistor Q1 conducts, Q2 is cut off. Then as Q2 conducts, Q1 is cut off. This seesaw action is accomplished as many times per second as desired, depending on the values of R1, C1, and R2, C2. The actual frequency is derived from the equation:

$$F \text{ ( frequency)} = \frac{1}{1.39 \times RC}$$

This is true when R1 equals R2 and C1 equals C2.

As the circuit stands, only one frequency can be produced. A single-tone generator has its uses and there are even commercial units offering one tone only. This is usually 1000 Hz, as that is the standard for many tests. However, a single tone will not be enough for many operations. An amplifier may pass and amplify a 1000 Hz tone and be unable to handle 5000 or 10,000 Hz frequencies. Consequently, we must be able to make our unit capable of creating other frequencies. To be able to vary the tones, many other combinations of R and C must be introduced into the circuit. This is done by a switch, usually a double-pole affair with as many positions as frequencies are wanted. The R-C combinations must then be calculated for each frequency desired.

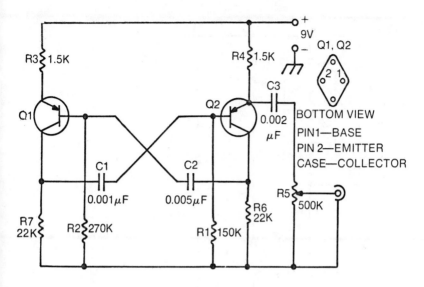

PARTS LIST
B1—9-volt transistor radio battery
C1—0.01μF tubular paper capacitor
C2—0.005μF tubular paper capacitor
C3—0.002μF tubular paper capacitor
Q1, Q2—G0005 general purpose PNP transistor (Radio Shack 276-2006. or equal)
R1—150.000 ohm carbon resistor
R2—270.000 ohm carbon resistor
R3, R4—1500 ohm carbon resistor
R5—500.000 ohm carbon resistor
R6·R7—22,000 ohm carbon resistor
All resistors 1 2 watt. 20% tolerance

Fig. 1-10. Simple multivibrator circuit.

Op amps make excellent portable signal generators. An example is the audio generator illustrated in Fig. 1-11. The double-pole three-position switch, S1 a-b, offers three different frequencies, one for each position. Resistor R4, a potentiometer, varies the output voltage. It will also have some effect on the wave shape. To obtain precise frequencies, capacitors C1 through C6 should be close tolerance units.

The reason for R4 is that it is necessary to reduce the output of the op amp to meet different needs. This means that the signal generator's output can be set to match the unit it is replacing in a test. There will be more about attenuators later, when the signal generator is described in detail.

So far, only the sine wave has been discussed. The reason for its wide use is that music is basically sinusoidal in character and therefore a sine wave most closely resembles the signal it is replacing in a music system.

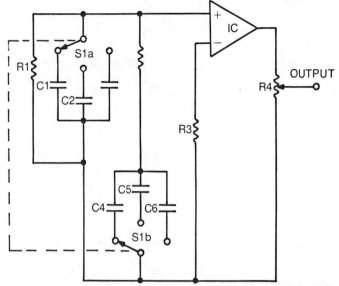

SIMPLIFIED CIRCUIT OF A TYPICAL OP AMP GENERATOR.
THE IC CAN BE A 741 FOR EXAMPLE; R1 IS EQUAL TO R2; R4 IS
A LINEAR TAPER POT. MANY OF THE COMPONENTS REQUIRED
FOR STABILITY HAVE BEEN INTENTIONALLY LEFT OUT, AS
HAS THE POWER SUPPLY.

Fig. 1-11. Typical op amp signal generator.

To understand the significance of a sine wave and how to
measure it, Fig. 1-12 should be studied. A sine wave represents
current flowing first in one direction and then the other. It
travels from positive to negative with a different value at each
given instant. The graph in Fig. 1-13 has the horizontal axis
laid out in seconds (time) while the vertical axis represents
voltage. In the example shown, the sine wave has a zero value
at zero seconds, as well as at five and nine seconds. At certain
times it reaches its peak value, which is shown by letter A in
the drawing. This peak value is 13 volts. But, five seconds later
it has reached the same value again, but now it is negative. A
sine wave goes as far up one half of a cycle as it goes down the
other half. In other words, a sine wave is a symmetrical wave.
The peak-to-peak voltage value is twice that of its peak value.

The Root Mean Square value (rms), also known as
"effective value" is represented by letter B. The rms value is
0.707 of the peak value. This is akin to saying that the peak
value is 1.414 of the effective value. The value of rms is
calculated as the square root of the average of the squares of

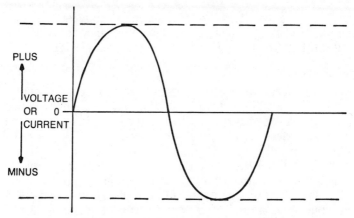

Fig. 1-12. Sine wave reaches equal values for plus and minus voltages.

the instantaneous amplitudes for one complete cycle of the wave.

The average value, as shown by letter C, is 0.636 of the peak value. While a signal generator usually measures its output voltage in rms values, an oscilloscope responds to P-P values.

But, not only can a sine wave be described in terms of voltage, it can also be described in terms of time. If it takes one microsecond to complete a full cycle of the wave, it is considered as having a frequency of one MHz. This is explained by: there are one million microseconds in a second

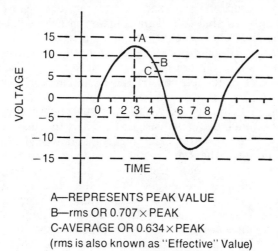

A—REPRESENTS PEAK VALUE
B—rms OR 0.707 × PEAK
C-AVERAGE OR 0.634 × PEAK
(rms is also known as "Effective" Value)

Fig. 1-13. Peak, rms, and average values of a sine wave.

29

and it takes only 1/1,000,000 of a second to complete a cycle, then we can say that in one second one million cycles will have occured. The frequency is therefore expressed as 1 MHz.

## Square Waves

The square wave offers certain advantages for testing circuits not available from the sine wave. A square wave alternates between two fixed values for equal lengths of time and furthermore is rich in odd-order harmonics. This allows us to test an amplifier employing only a few fundamental tones, but depending on the harmonics of that tone, is also able to furnish telltale information about the circuit we are testing. Let us say for example, that we inject a 1000 Hz square wave at the input of an amplifier. A square wave is made up of odd harmonics (1, 3, 5, 7, 9, etc.). It will appear sufficiently square when harmonics are present out to about the ninth. So, we are in effect testing the amplifier all the way up to about ten times the input frequency, or 10 kHz, when the fundamental applied tone is only 1000 Hz. If the square wave, as reproduced on the screen of the scope, shows rounding off—we can assume, quite correctly, that the amplifier is not capable of handling a 10 kHz·tone. A 2000 Hz signal would be pushing the upper limit of an amplifier rated at 10 kHz.

If you examine Fig. 1-14A, you will see a sine wave with its third harmonic. In Fig. 1-14B, the fifth harmonic is added and the seventh appears in Fig. 1-14C. The graph also shows how a square wave is made up of an infinite number of sine waves. With experience, one can examine the trace of a square wave and not only be able to tell that distortion exists, but which harmonic gives trouble to the circuit being tested.

There is still one more advantage to the use of a square wave for testing and that is the fact that this wave also shows what type of distortion caused the deviation from the ideal waveform.

Figure 1-15 illustrates various distorted square waves with the case of each distortion. Figure 1-15A is the ideal form of one cycle. The sides are perfectly straight lines and so are the top and bottom. The sides are perfectly vertical and the top and bottom are no less horizontal. To avoid any misconceptions, it should be noted that this is an ideal waveform—and few generators are able to produce such perfection. Whenever doing testing with any signal generator, it is important that the waveform as produced should be noted and memorized for comparison with the waveform after it has gone through the equipment being tested. This is why a dual-trace oscilloscope is a handy instrument to own. It shows

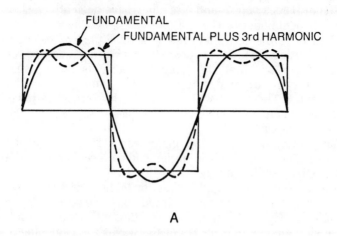

A

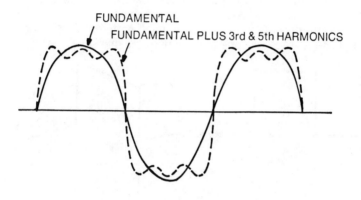

B

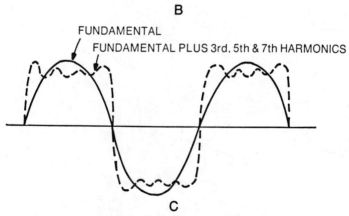

Fig. 1-14. Sine wave plus harmonics.

C

the signal traces before and after they have been affected by the component under test.

Figure 1-15B shows slight rounding off of the leading edge. This deviation, which is proportional to the degree of distortion, means that the tenth harmonic is not passing through the circuit under test with the same gain as the fundamental. The result will be that the low frequency tones will cover the higher frequencies. The cause of this is poor high frequency response.

The tilting in Fig. 1-15C indicates poor low frequency response. The phase shift is in the leading direction with the leading edges trailing down.

Phase shift in the lagging direction is shown in Fig. 1-15D. In this case, the leading edge is tilted up. The degree of tilt in this and in Fig. 1-15C indicates the amount of phase shift. Phase shift means that not all of the waves are beginning at the same time. This type of phase shift is of particular importance when testing a television receiver.

A coupling capacitor, whether open or too low in value, will cause a trace to appear similar to the one shown in Fig.

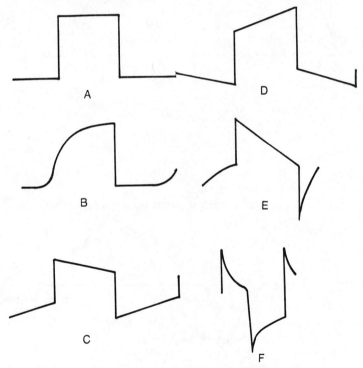

Fig. 1-15. Different types of distorted square waves.

1-15E. Differentiation has occured in this example. The phase of the output waveform is ahead of the input by 90 degrees. This type of phase shifting happens within an R-C network.

Excessive high frequency response will create a waveform resembling the one shown in Fig. 1-15F. This, in a sense, is the reverse of the distortion illustrated in Fig. 1-15B.

There is one disadvantage to the square wave for testing purposes: if an amplifier's input is connected to any sine wave source which overdrives that input, the sine wave is "clipped." The top and the bottom are cut off and the result appears to be a square wave. (See Fig. 1-16.) So, it pays to be careful of the amount of output voltage produced by the generator. It becomes too easy to confuse the "clipped" sine wave with the square wave. This is the reason for attenuators in the output circuit of the signal generators. One must remember that if a sine wave is fed to an amplifier, a sine wave must result at the output. It may be slightly or not at all distorted, but it must be a sine wave in some form.

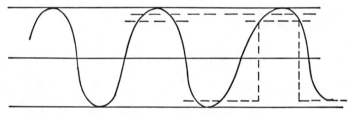

Fig. 1-16. Effects of "clipping" on a sine wave.

### Triangle Waves

Triangle waves are finding their uses as a means to troubleshoot electronic equipment. For the past several years, a controversy has been going on over the use of a sine wave as compared with a triangle wave, with no sharp conclusions being drawn from the arguments. It has been pointed out that distortion on a sine wave may be relatively high before it can be distinguished on the screen of an oscilloscope. (See Fig. 1-17). It may not be visible to trained eyes until as much as 5% distortion exists. Certainly, 2% distortion will escape most eyes. The answer to that charge is that many audio amplifiers have an inherent 2% distortion, so why should we be bothered with that amount appearing on the screen? This has been refuted by those who say that if we were able to test an amplifier in such a way as to make that 2% appear flagrant, then the amplifier manufacturers would be forced to reduce the distortion in their units. The technology is there, the critics

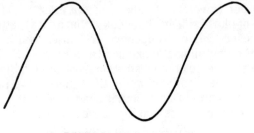

REFERENCE SINE WAVE

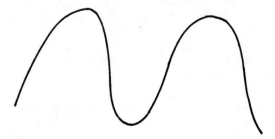

3% DISTORTION OVER ABOVE FIGURE

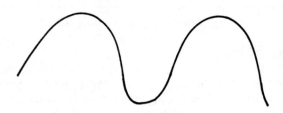

5% DISTORTION ABOVE REFERENCE

Fig. 1-17. Sine wave distortion.

say. It is true that manufacturers are bringing out hi-fi amplifiers with a reputed 0.025% THD (Total Harmonic Distortion).

So, the critics go on to say that the triangle wave should be employed, since a tiny amount of distortion is shown up in a glaring manner. It is easy to understand why. Instead of curves as in a sine wave, curves which are difficult to interpret, a triangle wave is composed of straight lines only. The sides of the triangle demand to be as straight as a ruler and the peaks must be as sharp as a pin. It is certainly true that any deviation from the straight line, due to distortion, is more easily recognized than a bulge in a curved line.

By a process known as "integrating", a triangle wave may be obtained from a square wave. An integrating circuit is one whose output waveform is the integral—in time—of the input waveform. Figure 1-18 shows this type of circuit. The values of the resistor and the capacitor can be varied for some interesting results. These results are well worth the effort of experimenting by introducing several values into the circuit. As is shown in Fig. 1-18, the output of a square wave generator is fed to this two-component circuit. The output of the integrator circuit is then connected to a scope's vertical input.

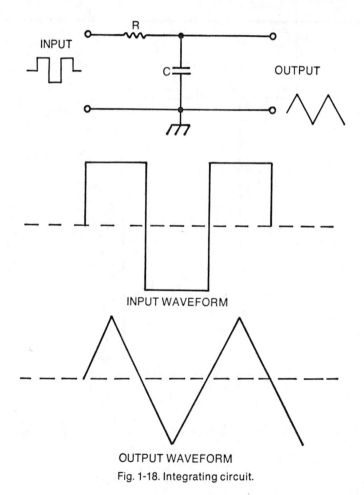

INPUT WAVEFORM

OUTPUT WAVEFORM

Fig. 1-18. Integrating circuit.

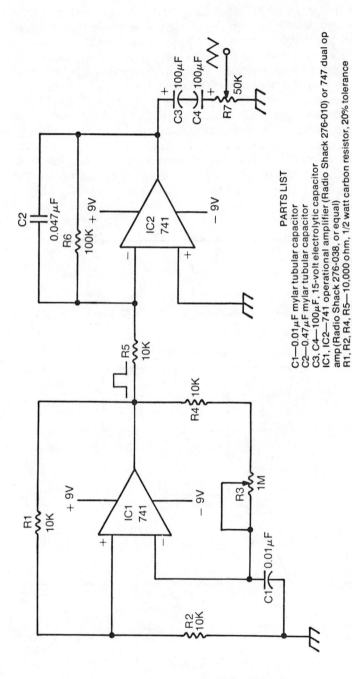

Fig. 1-19. Triangle wave generator.

PARTS LIST

C1—0.01μF mylar tubular capacitor
C2—0.47μF mylar tubular capacitor
C3, C4—100μF, 15-volt electrolytic capacitor
IC1, IC2—741 operational amplifier (Radio Shack 276-010) or 747 dual op amp (Radio Shack 276-038, or equal)
R1, R2, R4, R5—10,000 ohm, 1/2 watt carbon resistor, 20% tolerance
R3—1 Megohm potentiometer
R6—100,000 ohm, 1/2 watt carbon resistor, 20% tolerance
R7—50,000 ohm potentiometer

36

Why does this waveshape change occur? The theory in back of this concept is that a square wave, like a triangle wave, is made up of an infinite number of odd harmonics. As the capacitor is charged, and as the resistor acts upon the waveform, the harmonics are shifted about. However, the frequency of the wave remains the same.

For the sake of experimenting, if you are so inclined, you might try feeding the triangle wave into yet another integrator and see the results for yourself. You will find them interesting. However, all frequencies are not affected the same way, due to the harmonics of that frequency, so you will find that you may have to start at about 20 kHz and go up from there to observe the resulting waveforms.

The experimenter who would like a simple triangle wave generator should try the unit as shown in the schematic in Fig. 1-19. Two ICs are used, both of them the popular 741. There is a dual version of the 741, designated 747, which can be employed to replace both ICs in the circuit shown. The IC pin numbers should be studied, since they might be different from those indicated in the schematic. Components R1, R2, R3 and C1 determine the frequency and they need to be changed to obtain different time constants for different frequencies. A square wave can be tapped at R5. The second IC (or the other half of the 747) then converts this wave to a triangle wave of the same frequency. This unit is meant more for experimental uses than as a serious generator, since it lacks too many controls to be really of great use.

In the schematic of Fig. 1-20, we have still one more example of a dual-waveform generator which is also built around two ICs. In this case, the ICs are products of National Semiconductor and are the LM101A and LM107. The two outputs are like the previous unit, square and triangle waves. IC1 generates a square wave which is available at output Pin 6. R4, a 1-megohm potentiometer, controls the amplitude of the wave. You will note that Point A can be tapped to obtain a square wave varied in amplitude by R4, but not varied in frequency. It is the combination of R3 and the 150K-ohm potentiometer, R5, which varies the frequency. The square wave is connected to Pin 4, the negative input of IC2. This IC converts the square wave to a triangle wave obtainable at Pin 10, its output.

It is worth the experimenter's time to build or at least breadboard the unit. It is battery powered, requiring two 9-volt batteries in series to obtain the needed 18 volts. This supply must be double-ended since the LM101 and the LM107 require both plus and minus voltages. The schematic in Fig. 1-21A

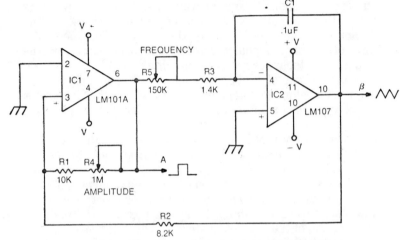

VOLTAGE IS DOUBLE-ENDED SUPPLY + 9 VOLT AND − 9
VOLT. NOTE THAT POINT A IS SQUARE WAVE OUTPUT, BUT
HAS NO FREQUENCY CONTROL—ONLY AMPLITUDE IS
VARIABLE. POINT β OFFERS TRIANGLE WAVE WITH BOTH
FREQUENCY AND AMPLITUDE CONTROLS.

PARTS LIST

C1—0.1μF mylar tubular capacitor
IC1—LM101A integrated circuit (National Semiconductor)
IC2—LM107 integrated circuit (National Semiconductor)
R1—10,000 ohm, 1/2 watt carbon resistor, 20% tolerance
R2—8200 ohm, 1/2 watt carbon resistor, 20% tolerance
R3—1400 ohm, 1/2 watt carbon resistor, 20% tolerance
R4—1 Megohm linear taper potentiometer
R5—150,000 ohm linear taper potentiometer

Fig. 1-20. Two IC waveform generator.

shows such a double-ended battery supply. The unit can, of
course, be connected to a line-powered supply (also
double-ended) as shown in Fig. 1-21B. Battery powered, this
unit makes an excellent little generator for simple field work
which may not be too demanding.

Much can be learned about generators by building even
these simple units. The output signal results can be observed
when different components are introduced into the circuit.
This is not possible with the commercially-built units, which do
not tolerate this internal surgery. Getting back to the
generators discussed above, instead of the continuously
variable attenuator, a series of resistors could be switched to
provide precise step attenuation. Before attempting that, it
would be of value to read the section on attenuators and why
they are *not* simply resistors thrown into the circuit to drop the
output voltage and consequently the amplitude of the wave.

Another word of caution: the first time the experimenter connects a signal generator to an amplifier and observes the results on the scope, he is usually astonished and saddened by the distorted trace. But, even the very best component introduces some distortion; even a piece of wire under certain conditions will distort a waveform. Before discouragement has set in and the amplifier is consigned to the interior darkness of a closet, make certain that it is not the signal generator that is at fault. It could even be the probes. A probe making poor contact can do horrible things to a perfectly formed wave. This is why all components of the testing chain should be held suspect until proven innocent. Means of checking these are shown among the projects in Chapter 3.

Must the hobbyist, or even the technician, have all three generators at hand? Or, does he even need all three waveforms? Naturally, it is better to have them and as we know, one waveform does not eliminate the need for the others. So the answer is a qualified "Yes". However, it is not necessary to have all three generators sitting on the workbench. Apart from the considerable cost involved, there

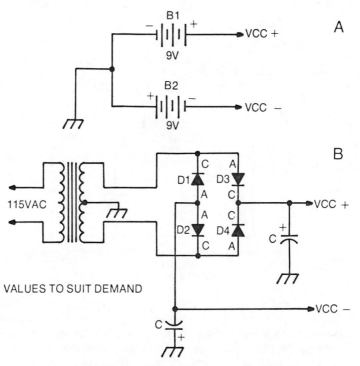

Fig. 1-21. Two types of double-ended supplies.

39

is always the matter of space to be considered. There are several options available to the worker: One—you can have sine wave generator with add-ons to produce other waveforms. Two—you can have a sine/square wave generator with an add-on for triangle waves. Most units on the market offering two waveforms are sine and square wave generators. Three—you can buy a function generator capable of creating all three waveforms, and in some cases able to generate all three simultaneously.

Going back to the first option, you can use a simple add-on circuit to the sine wave generator and get a square wave. This circuit is shown in Fig. 1-22. An IC, the 555 chip, is the brains of the unit. The circuit produces a Schmitt trigger. It is important that the sine wave be of sufficient amplitude to be greater than the reference voltage needed to trigger the 555. When it is triggered, the internal flip-flop of the 555 goes on and off without changing the frequency as set by the sine wave generator. Actually, what it does is square the original sine wave.

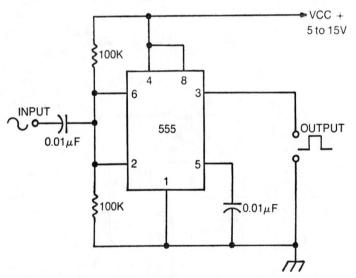

Fig. 1-22. Sine-to-square wave converter.

You will note in the following chapter several companies that offer generators capable of putting out square and sine waves, with some units producing both simultaneously. This can be a decided advantage in certain types of troubleshooting.

In the past, all generators were tube types, and therefore quite bulky. Now that we have ICs with their integrated components on one chip, the units have been reduced to a fraction of their former size, thus making them extremely handy for field work.

Several manufacturers have developed ICs which are designed expressly for the purpose of generating waveforms. Intersil's 8038 is such an example. The 8038 is a 14-pin DIP which offers three waveforms simultaneously. These are the old standbys: sine, square and triangle waves. As the schematic in Fig. 1-23 shows, the internal circuitry of the 8038 is extremely complex, but it is this internal complexity which ultimately simplifies the work of the hobbyist in putting this IC to work in a generator.

In Fig. 1-24, we have a block diagram of the Intersil 8038 3-way function generator. Only capacitor C1 is external to the IC in this diagram. This capacitor is alternately charged and discharged by two current sources: Current Source One is on all of the time, while Current Source Two is continuously switching from on to off by a flip-flop.

When the flip-flop cuts off Source Two, the capacitor becomes charged only by Current Source One and current I. As a result, the voltage across the capacitor rises linearly with time. When the voltage across the capacitor reaches a threshold voltage of Comparator One (this action is similar to that of another IC, the 555) the flip-flop changes state and turns on Current Source Two, which carries a current of 2I. It should not be forgotten that the threshold voltage of Comparator One is 2/3 of the supply voltage. As the capacitor is discharged with current I, the voltage across it drops linearly with time. The capacitor now begins to discharge toward a negative value; it eventually reaches the threshold voltage of Comparator Two, which is set at 1/3 of the supply voltage. At the moment this occurs, the comparator output kicks the flip-flop back to its original state and Current Source Two is turned off. The cycle then repeats.

The square wave output comes from the flip-flop and then goes to another buffer amplifier whose collector is connected to output 9. The supply voltage for the square wave is thus independent of the rest of the circuitry. TTL compatibility may be provided by means of a separate 5-volt supply.

Developed across C1, the triangle waveform is fed internally to a buffer amplifier. The same waveform also goes to a sine wave converter by means of a nonlinear network.

There are only three trim pots, six resistors and two capacitors to be mounted on the PC board itself, plus a socket for the IC. The frequency control, R3, would be mounted on the front panel of the unit.

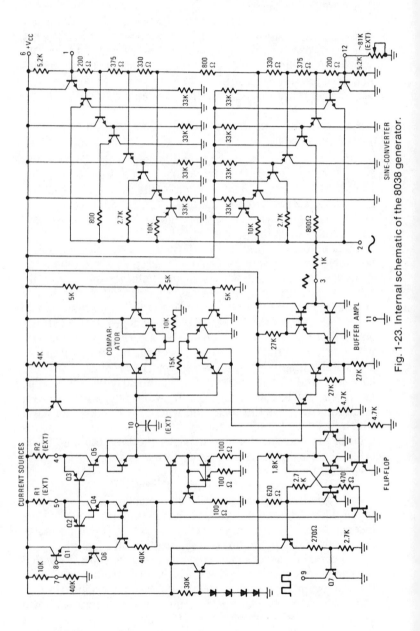

Fig. 1-23. Internal schematic of the 8038 generator.

42

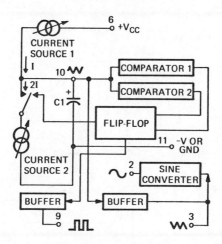

NOTE: ONLY CAPACITOR C1
IS EXTERNAL TO THE IC.

Fig. 1-24. Block diagram of the 8038 generator.

The circuit for the 3-way function generator is illustrated in Fig. 1-25.

The output frequency will always be the same for all three waveforms since they are obtainable simultaneously. This frequency is determined basically by the two timing components C1 and R3. In the circuit, R3 is a potentiometer which offers a range of frequencies from 20 Hz to 20 kHz. If this range, either at the top or at the bottom, is not sufficient, the circuit is flexible enough to be adjusted to suit one's particular purpose. C1 can be changed, either to a unit of a different value, or to a series of switched values. It must be remembered that increasing the value of C1 will lower the ouput frequency and substituting a smaller value will result in a higher frequency. Mica capacitors are recommended when the value of C1 is reduced. When increasing the value of this component to inordinately large amounts, it is important to make certain that the capacitor, in this case it would be an electrolytic, is not leaking an undue amount of current. With a large enough capacitor, a frequency of one cycle an hour can be obtained!

The unit should be encased in a metal or a plastic box. There should be four terminals: one for each waveform and the fourth for the ground which is common to all of the outputs. The front panel of the case should also have the frequency adjust pot and an ON-OFF switch.

Two 9-volt batteries can be used to operate the function generator for a reasonably long period of time since the

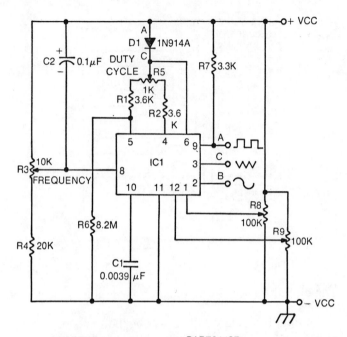

PARTS LIST

C1—0.0039μF mylar tubular capacitor
C2—0.1μF, 25-volt electrolytic capacitor
D1—1N914A silicon diode (Radio Shack 276-1144, or equal)
IC1—3-way function generator IC (Intersil 8038CC)
R1, R2—3600 ohm, 1/4 watt carbon resistor, 10% tolerance
R3—10,000 ohm linear taper potentiometer
R4—20,000 ohm, 1/4 watt carbon resistor, 10% tolerance
R5—1000 ohm linear taper trimpot
R6—8.2 Megohm, 1/4 watt carbon resistor, 10% tolerance
R7—3300 ohm, 1/4 watt carbon resistor, 10% tolerance
R8, R9—100,000 ohm linear taper trimpot

Parts Kit available from:
Photolume Corporation
118 E. 28th Street
New York, N.Y. 10016
$10.95 including PC board

Fig. 1-25. Single IC 3-way function generator.

current drain is approximately 12 to 15 mA. (The circuit for this double-ended battery supply is shown in Fig. 1-21A.) If the use of the generator is limited to the workbench, the power supply in Fig. 1-26 can be substituted. The supply is zener-regulated, but other versions of a regulated supply may be used instead, provided that it does not go over the manufacturer's recommended upper limit of ± 15 VDC for the 8038.

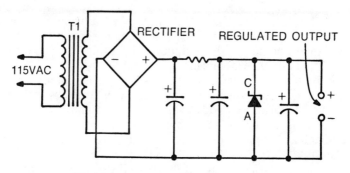

Fig. 1-26. Typical regulated power supply.

Adjustment of the unit can now be done, once the few parts are soldered to the PC board. The use of a board is suggested over point-to-point wiring, since it simplifies construction time greatly and avoids the possibility of mistakes and incorrect operation of the unit. A scope should be connected first to the triangle waveform output (output C on the schematic). The trimpot, R5, should be slowly adjusted until a duty cycle is produced which reveals a triangle wave similar to the one shown in Fig. 1-27. The probe from the scope is now moved to the output marked B. Observe the sine wave output as R8 and R9 are adjusted. There is reaction between the two trimpots, so the adjustment has to be repeated until a sine wave is obtained which ressembles the one shown in Fig. 1-27. Move the probe to the point marked A on the board, which is the output for the square wave. The square wave at this moment should now have a duty cycle of 50%. This means that it is on as much as it is off; the base line is equal in length (i.e., time)

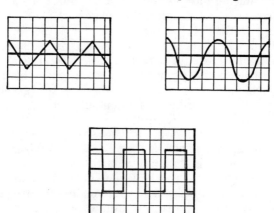

Fig. 1-27. Waveform outputs from Intersil 8038.

45

to the top line. (See Fig. 1-27) Some minor adjustment might be necessary, so R5 should be retouched carefully. Be aware that overloading of the outputs will result in introducing distortion into the waveforms.

Photolume Corporation makes the whole kit available which contains all the necessary parts with the PC board. This function generator is ready to build and sells for $10.95. For the price, it is a very respectable generator just as it stands, although an attenuator circuit could be added to make it more adaptable.

The same IC, the Intersil 8038, was the subject of an article which appeared in the October 1973 issue of Popular Electronics, by-lined by the author. John Paul, who evolved the circuit, combined this IC with two others to produce a generator able to offer a choice of three waveforms up to 100 kHz, with both logarithmic and linear sweep.

## Sweep Generators

Why sweep generators? It is of primary importance to know the frequency versus the amplitude of many linear circuits. This will include filters, equalizers, tuned circuits and selective amplifiers. Measurements are carried out as shown in several setups in the chapter on projects. The method consists of connecting a variable signal generator to the input of the circuit under test and using a meter or scope to measure the output. With an ordinary signal generator, measurements are made at as many frequencies as possible to obtain enough points to plot a graph, which will be comprehensive enough to show the overall performance picture. By using a sweep generator and a scope, it is possible to show a graph on the CRT which will indicate gain or loss versus frequency.

The operation of a sweep generator is as follows: A sawtooth voltage is applied to the oscilloscope and sweeps the electron beam across the screen so a horizontal deflection is obtained, which is proportional to a time base. The Y-deflection (vertical) is proportional to the generator's output amplitude so, if the scope's output is uniform, a plot of gain versus frequency will result.

If the sweep generator has a linear sweep, the frequency of any point on the graph can be read directly. The disadvantage of the linear sweep is that only a narrow section of the audio band will be shown in any degree of detail. In a 10 kHz sweep, the bass and midrange, which account for the frequencies from roughly 20 to 1000 Hz, are jammed into the first 10% of the sweep while the balance, 90%, covers the treble frequencies in detail.

This is solved by use of a logarithmic sweep. Each band has an equal spread on the CRT. The rate of frequency change with time increases at a constant pace.

Other sweep generators are illustrated in the chapter on manufacturers' generators. The use of the sweep generator is explained in more detail in that part of the book which describes the operation of various generators.

For the experimenter who is in the market for a signal generator which is commercially built, it would pay to read the manufacturers' specifications which accompany each photograph. It makes comparative shopping relatively easy. However, one should be careful not to make the mistake of comparing apples and oranges. Each sine wave generator is not exactly like any other, whether it be made by another manufacturer or even another model made by the same manufacturer. The list of manufacturers is by no means complete. Those included were chosen arbitrarily as they exemplified, in the author's view, some particular feature and this does not mean that other models do not have that same feature, but they may have lacked something else, or the price might have been in another range and therefore not truly comparable.

## OSCILLATORS

This section deals with non-sine wave oscillators. The reason for the amount of space devoted to the subject is that oscillators in one form or another create the waveforms which are used in a signal generator. By understanding the principles of the various oscillators, one can better learn how to use or modify circuits to produce the desired waveforms—or at least to understand what makes a generator tick. This is of special value with the square, triangle, or even the more complex waveforms.

By experimenting in the production of a variety of waveforms, the hobbyist can obtain a surprising amount of knowledge in how waveforms are formed, how they are affected by shorted, open, or wrong-value components. Only with experience can one recognize the difference, for example, between a clipped sine wave and true square wave, how overloading an input can create odd traces on the scope, and other effects which are not mentioned even in books on oscilloscopes. Only practical experience can provide the full gamut of learning which is what the technician or hobbyist needs to fully understand, enjoy and profit from electronics. Much can be gained—painlessly—through the building and converting of circuits and seeing for yourself the results by using a signal generator and a scope or VTVM. Oscillators, particularly of the non-sinusoidal type, are of immeasureable value.

### Relaxation Oscillators

This type of oscillator produces an output waveform that fluctuates between two limits, which is not sinusoidal—this oscillator produces pulses instead—its gain being greater than unity. This is a class of oscillators in which the circuit operates in transition between two blocked, or overloaded end-states, caused by a large excess of positive feedback. A relaxation oscillator can be stable, in which case the circuit is in one condition until it is externally pulsed, or triggered, or quasi-stable, recovering after a certain period which is determined by a time constant in a coupling circuit. After that period is over, the circuit will switch back to its opposite state. There are three classes of relaxation oscillators: bistable, monostable, astable. Each class is determined by the number of stable end-states.

Many circuits are adaptable to all three classes; this permits a wide assortment of circuits to be created, including multivibrators, blocking oscillators, trigger circuits and counter circuits. Relaxation oscillators are widely used for counting and frequency division, triggering and similar types of applications. However, the end use which most interests us is that the relaxation oscillator is able to generate a wide range of non-sinusoidal waveforms.

### Bistable Oscillators

As the name suggests, this oscillator has two stable states; when Q1 in Fig. 1-28 is on, Q2 is off, thus supplying a positive triggering pulse to the base of Q1, cutting it off with negative voltage now going from the collector to the base of Q2, which now conducts. This state continues until another triggering pulse is applied to the base of Q2. An asymetrical multivibrator circuit is used as a triggering device, and this is especially useful in pulse generators. To switch Q1 on, an impulse voltage is raised to a value which will make Q1 conduct, and by reducing, to cut off. A pulse is generated when the input signal crosses above or below a given value.

### Monostable Oscillators

This type of multivibrator is a flip-flop with one stable state. It is achieved if one coupling impedence is resistive and the other capacitive. Q1 with its capacitive coupling is conducting, while Q2 is cut off with resistive coupling and negative voltage.

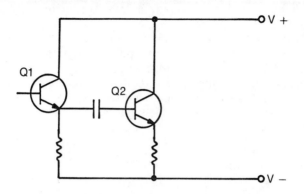

Fig. 1-28. Bistable oscillator (simplified).

When this circuit is triggered, a single output pulse is obtained whose length is set by the time constant. When Q1 is switched on for a saturated operation, it must go through three separate conditions. It should be understood, of course, that these conditions are almost instantaneous. These conditions are:

    a. Q1 is off, the base-emitter junction is reverse biased and the only current flowing through the capacitor circuit is the leakage curent, in which case $I_C = I_{CEO}$
    b. Transistor is operating and $I_C = I_{CEO} + (h_{FE})(I_B)$
    c. Q1 is saturated with the result that $I_C = I_{SAT}$

## Astable Multivibrators

An astable multivibrator consists of a circuit that has no stable state; it alternates automatically between two unstable end-states. This continues as long as power is connected to the circuit. One tube or one transistor conducts and is cut off for intervals of time determined by the circuit constants, while the other tube or transistor is cut off. The process is reversed with the second element conducting when the first tube or transistor is cut off. The frequency is dependent on the time constants. An astable multivibrator requires no external trigger, which is why it is also known as a free-running multivibrator. This type of multivibrator can be very easily synchronized at the frequency of any constantly repeating input signal. An example of such a multivibrator is discussed in detail with the 555 IC. A blocking oscillator is a typical example of an astable multivibrator.

**Pulse Forming.** An input pulse can be transformed to a pulse of a desired duration and amplitude, making the circuit valuable for driving sweep, pulse and timing wave generators.

By integrating the pulse output sweep, waveforms can be produced.

**Counting.** Once this circuit is triggered, another triggering action will not affect the original pulse during its length. This makes it have great importance for counting.

**Delay.** The trailing edge of the output waveform (see Fig. 1-29) can be used to provide a pulse which is delayed by a certain length of time from the input pulse. Since the duration of the output waveform can be controlled, a variable delay is obtainable.

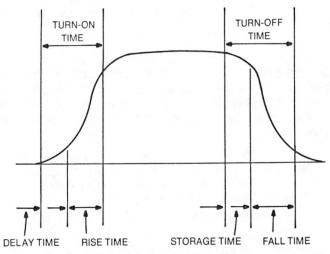

Fig. 1-29. Description of pulse waveform.

If there is a great difference in the bias voltage, many of these circuits can be converted to the monostable type.

Tubes have been described in some of these circuits and so have transistors. Although a tube is a high input impedence device and the transistor a low impedence component, essentially the same circuits have been used with both tubes and the so-called solid state devices. The field effect transistors (FETs) with their high input impedence were found to be able to be substituted almost directly for tubes. Although theoretically ideal, there was a distinct disadvantage when using an FET. It tends to be noisy. This, of course, negates its value in circuits in which noise of the unit under test is being measured or where the noise of the FET can cause false triggering. Stability, or rather lack of it, was another flaw shown by the FET. Now that ICs have made their appearance, several are designed precisely for oscillator circuits. One such is the 555, which is both an oscillator and timing device. It is worth studying in detail. Figure 1-30 shows the internal logic of this versatile IC.

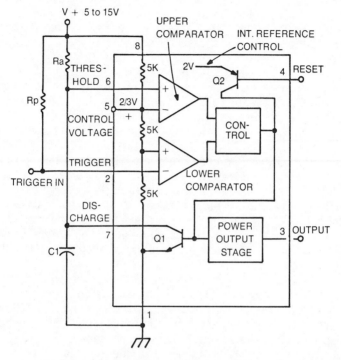

Fig. 1-30. Internal schematic of 555.

The basic mode of operation of the 555 is that of a one-shot timer, triggered externally with either a positive or a negative pulse. This is of great importance for our purpose since it provides excellent oscillation of non-sinusoidal waveforms, equal to what one might expect from relaxation oscillator. While the internal elements of the 555 are relatively complex, the needed external components to operate the unit consist only of one resistor and one capacitor. For stable operation as an oscillator, the free running frequency and the duty cycle are both accurately controlled by a minimum of external components: two resistors and one capacitor. The internal circuit provides control, triggering, level sensing and discharge. From the power output stage, a high-level gate is available while the timing is in progress. This gate is almost equal to the voltage used to drive the unit, ranging from 5 to 15 VDC.

In its first, or standby state, Q1 is conducting. This clamps the external capacitor C1 to ground potential. Three 500-ohm resistors form an internal bias divider with the resulting bias voltages, which are 2/3 and 1/3 of the input voltage respectively. These voltages are then fed to the upper and lower limit comparators. It is these two voltages which determine the voltage thresholds and which control the timing interval.

The lower comparator is, as we said, biased at 1/3 of the input voltage, and therefore stays in its standby state as long as the trigger input (pin 2) is held higher than this voltage. When this triggering input goes low, the flip-flop is set by the lower comparator. This turns off Q1 and the output goes to its high state, which is almost equal to the input voltage. The capacitor Q1 is now unclamped and it charges through the resistor. $R_A$, exponentially toward $V+$. After a period of time, which is dependent on the time constant set by $R_A$ and C1, the voltage across the capacitor reaches 2/3 the value of the input voltage. This is the threshold of the upper comparator. The flip-flop is now reset by the upper comparator, turning on Q1, discharging C1 to zero and returning the output to the standby state.

The 555 has several advantages to offer the experimenter of oscillator circuits: (1) the input voltage can vary greatly, (2) any additional triggering during a timing interval will not affect the cycle, providing the additional trigger is of shorter duration than the timing cycle, (3) by applying a low-level input at pin 4, Q1 is turned off and the output pulse is terminated, (5) the upper threshold voltage is available at pin 5, allowing external control of the pulse width. It is possible to use the 555 to produce excellent square waves with varying duty cycles, or even as a pulse generator.

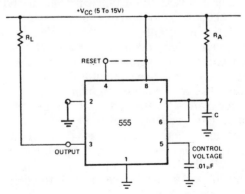

Fig. 1-31. Monostable application of the 555.

If the 555 is used in the triggered monostable mode, it should be wired as shown in Fig. 1-31. The precise values for desired time delays can be obtained from Fig. 1-32. Charge and discharge times, as well as frequency, are independent of the supply voltage.

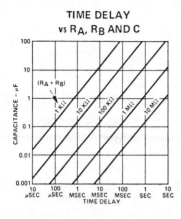

Fig. 1-32. Time delay chart for 555.

By connecting the 555 as shown in Fig. 1-33, the unit will trigger itself and run in the astable mode. The duty cycle can be precisely set merely by adjusting the ratio between $R_A$ and $R_B$. Again, the frequency is independent of voltage. Free running frequency is set with the values indicated in Fig. 1-34.

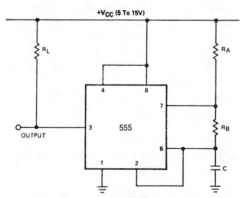

Fig. 1-33. Astable application of the 555.

The experimenter who wishes to go further into the 555 may want to use the chip as a pulse-width modulator by using one 555 as the clock generator, which determines the pulse width of the second 555. The output pulses will have a

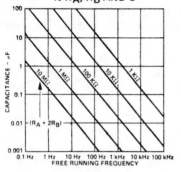

**FREE RUNNING FREQUENCY**
**vs R$_A$, R$_B$ AND C**

Fig. 1-34. Frequency chart for 555.

frequency equal to the clock input frequency, while the pulse width is controlled by the modulating signal.

The same IC makes a fine electronic switch to convert a simple oscilloscope to a dual-trace unit. The 555 acts as a square wave generator which switches two amplifiers to the common output on the scope. The result, due to the rapid switching and the retention of the image by the eyes, is two traces appearing to be simultaneous.

As is readily understood, any square wave generator could be used for the above purposes; the 555 merely offers more options, and is easier to handle due to the small number of components needed to vary frequency, amplitude and duty cycles. This is a marked advantage to the experimenter in that he can truly experiment without worrying about what will result should he apply the wrong voltage to the unit. The cost of ruining the IC is negligible compared with the cost of a commercial square wave generator.

Several other ICs, designed either for the purpose of generating waveforms, converted for that use, are discussed in the chapter discussing the various types of generators.

**POWER SUPPLIES**

A source of voltage in one form or another is necessary to power both the oscillator and the amplifying stages of the signal generator. In the days of the tubes there was little choice in power supplies: usually power was derived from the 115 VAC line, or an A and B battery was employed—which is why we still write about B+ voltages. Then, a transformer was used to produce the several voltages: one usually at 6.3 VAC which supplied the voltage for the tube filaments, another section of the transformer stepped up the voltage to whatever level was needed to power the tubes; this could be from 150 to 600 volts. (See Fig. 1-35A.)

54

Now that transistors and ICs have replaced the tubes to a certain degree, the power supply is reduced in many cases to no more than a single 9-volt battery. (Fig. 1-35B.) Some ICs, which require a doubled-ended supply, will be fed by two batteries in series, tapped at their common point to achieve ground potential. (This was illustrated in Fig. 1-21B.) There are times when the batteries are not sufficient. There may be too many transistors, or the IC may need more current than can be conveniently supplied by a battery or two. In those cases, one has to go back to using the line voltage as the sources.

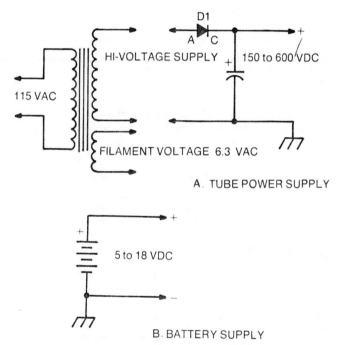

Fig. 1-35. Two types of power supplies.

Although similar to the power supply for driving tubes, for low voltage devices it is much simpler. A transformer steps down to 115 VAC to whatever voltage is needed, usually under 30 volts. One, two, or four diodes are employed as rectifiers to change the AC voltage to pulsating DC, which the transistors see the same as they would true DC from a battery.

Many ICs have filtering components built within the chip which eliminated the need for any filtering. But for transistors, which do not have that built-in facility, one or two large capacitors filter the voltage to reduce troublesome hum.

Figure 1-36 shows a typical single-ended power supply operated from the 115 VAC line. Figure 1-21B is a double-ended supply.

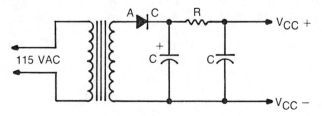

Fig. 1-36. Single-ended line supply.

Any solid state generator which draws no more than 10 mA can be powered by a battery without the need to replace it too often. Once the current demand rises above that figure, it becomes necessary to power by means of the type of supply outlined previously.

Some transistors and ICs require the use of a regulated supply which does not vary from a given voltage level regardless of the current being drawn. Zeners or a solid state regulator will be employed for current and/or voltage limiting. Figure 1-37 illustrates an example of the regulated supply.

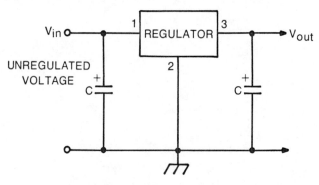

Fig. 1-37. Power supply using regulator.

## MODULATOR CIRCUIT

A modulator circuit is found only in RF generators, since a audio generator has no need of modulation. Therefore, the RF generator has two oscillator circuits: one for generating an audio frequency and the other a radio frequency. These two frequencies are blended together with a vacuum tube acting as the blender. The AF frequency goes to the grid of the tube while the RF is connected to the plate. The mixed, or modulated, signal is now seen at the plate circuit. From the plate, this combined signal is now fed to the attenuator circuit.

## ATTENUATORS

In the simple circuits shown to illustrate the workings of a transistor or IC oscillator, the output was at a constant level. In other words, the signal level was at one uniform point. Such a generator would be of limited value. Output must be able to be varied over a fairly wide signal level. For example, the table below shows the different outputs associated with the various signal sources:

| Source | Level |
|---|---|
| Moving coil microphone | 0.25mV |
| Dynamic phono cartridge | 5 mV |
| Ceramic phono cartridge | 300 mV |
| Crystal phono cartridge | 500 mV |
| Radio receiver | 250 mV |

So, if we are to test a preamplifier, for example, and we want to know whether it is sensitive enough to reproduce a signal whose input level is no more than 5 mV, we must be able to attenuate or reduce the signal from our generator so that it, too, is no more than 5 mV. The level of the generator must be capable of matching any of the signal sources listed above—and more.

To obtain these signal levels, an attenuator circuit is added just before the output of the generator. While these attenuators control the signal levels, they must also maintain a constant output impedence. There are two types of attenuators: continous or stepping. The continuous type uses a potentiometer, similar to the volume control on a radio, while the step attenuators use a series of fixed resistors, as in the circuit shown in Fig. 1-38. The signal level will decrease in fixed amounts, but the resistor arrangement provides the same output impedance at each step. It is essential that the output cable from the signal generator is terminated with a resistor whose value is equal to the characteristic impedance of the coaxial cable. If coax is not used, the resistor is left out.

The switch positions in most attenuator circuits are marked in dB, as well as in voltage level. A dB, or decibel, can be defined as the level of a pure sine wave whose change in level is barely detectable by the average human ear. The difference in decibels between two signals is 20 times the common logarithm of their ratio of voltages. For example, Hewlett Packard's Model 204D Oscillator has an attenuator

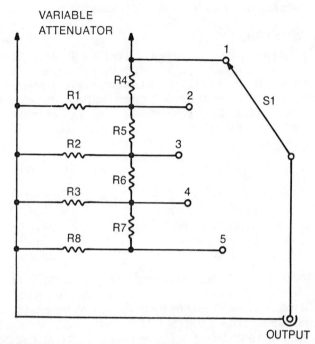

VARIABLE
ATTENUATOR

IN POSITION 1 FULL OUTPUT IS OBTAINED. THE RESISTORS
ARE CHOSEN TO PROVIDE EQUAL INCREMENTS BETWEEN
STEPS OF S1. TYPICAL SETTINGS FOR THE SWITCH MIGHT
PROVIDE THESE OUTPUT VALUES:

1—10V
2—3V
3—1V

Fig. 1-38. Attenuator circuit.

switch in which its highest position is indicated as +10 dB or
2.5 volts. Its lowest point is a signal with a level of −70 dB or
250 mV. Each step is in −10 dB increments.

The electronic industry has adopted the standard that 0 dB
is equal to 1 milliwatt at 600 ohms. With an external load of 600
ohms, the reference level is automatically defined. If the load
varies greatly from the 600 ohms, then correction factors must
be calculated. This is in the case where precise measurements
are needed.

But, in many cases, since a dB is a *relative* value it is
really unimportant to know the exact load.

As an example: We are testing a preamplifier to learn if it
will amplify a small signal on the order of 0.01 volt. We set the
generator so that it is producing exactly a signal of that level,

which is equal to −40dB. When this signal is injected into the preamp, we read (on our VTVM) an output level from the preamp of 10 volts or +20 dB. Since it takes 40 dBs to go to 0, we add the 40 to the 20 and we can now say that the preamplifier is cabable of a 60 dB increase.

In many generators there is also an output control with a meter so that precise values, between those of the attenuator switch, can be set. The meter will be marked in volts and in dB. These values will be added or subtracted to the values from the markings on the attenuator switch. The meter is built into the circuit so it is reading the voltage at the output. Not all manufacturers use a meter to indicate the output level. One can do without it, unless precise measurements are being taken, as was pointed out above. Even then, to know that the signal being injected at one particular step is usually enough.

## PROBES

Simple as they seem, probes can be all too often a mystifying source of problems. The cable connecting the probe to the signal generator may break, due to constant flexing of the wire, and create unusual waveforms. We remember once when waveforms were appearing and disappearing on the face of the CRT like Northern Lights. Was the amplifier going into orbit? After shutting off the power in haste, the cause of the intermittent traces was found to be that the cable end had partially slipped out of the banana jack. Then, the solder joint between the cable and the probe may break and not be immediately noticed. This can occur either at the generator-end of the cable or at the probe-end. So, it pays to notice the condition of the cables.

The direct probe consists of two wires, one from the "hot" side terminating with a metal tip and the other fastened to the case of the generator and terminated with an alligator clip, which is connected to the chassis of the unit under test (only, of course, if the chassis is at ground potential). Better probes will include a cable made up of flexible wire surrounded by a woven wire shield. This shield is connected to the ground side and prevents stray capacitances which are apt to cause erroneous traces or readings. Induced by an unshielded wire, these capacitances show up as noise on the VTVM and will create peculiar waveforms on the scope.

The direct probe is used to connect the generator, which is producing audio frequency tones, to a unit being tested. As long as we deal with audio frequencies or low radio frequencies, the direct probe is adequate. It is employed in 90% of signal generation.

When dealing with higher radio frequencies, demodulator probes are mandatory. This probe goes under many aliases, depending on its internal circuit. It can be called a modulator, detector, high frequency or an RF probe. The name depends pretty much on the actual design of the components inside the probe. A demodulator probe should be of the construction recommended by the manufacturer of the generator. It will best match the output impedance, frequency range and output voltage of the unit.

This probe, regardless of its name, reduces the loading effect of the signal generator onto a critical and sensitive circuit. It also minimizes regeneration and is of great help in limiting noise pickup, hum and radiation from the connecting cable. As was mentioned above, these problems are of minor importance when dealing with audio frequencies, but these effects become all too apparent with higher frequencies. For example, to inject a tone into an I-F amplifier with a direct probe would result in the circuit not operating at all or very poorly—and it would not be the fault of the I-F circuit.

If there is any doubt about the reaction of the direct probe to the frequencies being employed, place your hand or body against the probe. If the waveform changes, or the reading on the VTVM goes up, there is a good argument for using a demodulator probe.

Probes used in the RF ranges employ coaxial cable to prevent pickup of stray capacitances and use a coaxial connector to reduce possibility of hum at the output of the generator. This type of screw-in connector is far more dependable than the banana plugs commonly found. In audio generators, these cheap plugs are generally used and prove to be a misplaced enconomy. There is no reason why the cable, of whatever type, should not be a permanent part of the generator. The apparent saving in having one cable serve for a multitude of uses is slight and hardly compensates for the trouble caused by a loose fitting plug.

**FREQUENCY RANGES**

Signal generators fall into two broad classifications: Audio Frequency (AF) and Radio Frequency (RF). Audio frequencies are those that are audible to the human ear. These range from about 15 Hz up to about 10 kHz or 12 kHz. But, most audio equipment will have specifications that indicate that the upper range is 20 kHz. One might well ask the point of having equipment that produces music that cannot be heard. Reason: the overtones existing in music, or even in the human voice, lend "color" to the fundamental frequency or tone. It is the difference between hearing music over the telephone, with its extremely limited audio range, and hearing the same music over high fidelity equipment. So, it is important that an amplifier or reciever is capable of going above the audible range, thus reproducing the harmonics which add color and timbre to sounds. Research has found that women can generally hear higher tones better than men, so it is not surprising when a lady asks to have the hi-fi turned down since her ears are susceptible to a range of tones not heard by the males. Furthermore, as one gets older, the audible range becomes compressed and the higher tones cannot be heard.

But, whether these tones can be heard or not, they can be seen on an oscilloscope, so the average audio generator should be capable of producing tones within that range with a fairly constant output and with a minimum of distortion. The better units—which also means the more expensive ones—are capable of going far above the upper limits of that range.

Radio frequencies (RF) are those tones above the reach of the human ear. These are the frequencies that surround us and can only be heard by a radio receiver or television reciever (among others). The action of these receivers is to convert the frequencies into af and amplify them so they can be heard or seen.

Radio frequencies are designated by the Federal Communications Commission as follows:

Very-Low (VLF) ................................ below 30 kHz
Low (LF) ........................................... 30—300 kHz
Medium (MF) .................................... 300—3000 kHz
High (HF) .......................................... 3—30 MHz
Very-High (VHF) ............................... 30—300 MHz
Ultra-High (UHF) ............................. 300—3,000 MHz
Super-High (SHF) ............................ 3,000—30,000 MHz
Extremely-High (EHF) .................. 30,000—300,000 MHz

It is doubtful that any hobbyist is going to work anywhere within those latter regions, but with electronics making such fast progress, it is dangerous to predict the future in this forward-marching science. It was not so many years ago that a very good tape recorder was only able to reach, according to the manufacturer's own specifications, 12,000 Hz at a tape speed of 7.5 inches-per-second (ips). Today, that limit has been surpassed at 3.75 ips. So, who can predict at what extremes the hobbyist will be operating his equipment in a few years?

All RF signal generators do not operate up to the same limits. Looking at specification sheets for four RF signal generators, one reads these ranges:

| Eico | 150 kHz to 145 MHz |
|------|-------------------:|
| Heath | 100 kHz to 220 MHz |
| Hewlett Packard | 500 kHz to 100 MHz |
| Marconi | 10 kHz to 510 MHz |

It is obvious that some units are capable of generating a broader range of frequencies than others. This, however, is not a figure of merit. It means that either for the customers' needs, or for an engineering reason, the unit is designed to encompass only those frequencies. There are other factors to be considered than just the range of the instrument. Farther along, each of these factors will be discussed in detail.

Although two categories of frequencies were mentioned, there is a third which lies within the RF range. This consists of intermediate frequencies, or I-F. This group of signals is generated by combining a signal received by a superheterodyne receiver and its own local oscillator. The FCC has designated the AM (Amplitude Modulation) broadcast band to extend from 535 kHz to 1605 kHz. These are the "carrier" frequencies and they are assigned in multiples of 10 kHz between 540 and 1600 kHz. The FM (Frequency Modulation) broadcast band extends from 88 MHz to 108 MHz. Each broadcast channel is 200 kHz wide. Television uses two sets of frequencies, one for video and the other for audio. A TV set must encompass frequencies from 54 MHz to 890 MHz. Each channel is 6 MHz wide, while the video carrier is 4.5 MHz lower than the center aural frequency. (This is 0.25 MHz lower than the upper frequency of each channel).

The assigned TV frequencies are:

| Channels 2 through 4 | 54 to 72 MHz |
|----------------------|-------------:|
| Channels 5 and 6 | 76 to 88 MHz |
| Channels 7 through 13 | 172 to 216 MHz |
| Channels 14 through 83 | 470 to 890 MHz |

By studying the tables, you can see that all of the FM stations lie between Channels 6 and 7.

This information has been presented to show that whenever testing a receiver, whether AM, FM, or TV, and RF generator must be able to simulate these frequencies.

There is no sharp delineation between AF and RF. For example, while the upper limit of the audio range is defined as ending at 20 kHz with the RF range beginning at 30 kHz, there is no 10 kHz gap as would seem to exist at first glance. In actuality, some RF generators are capable of going as low as 10 kHz while some AF generators can rise above 100 kHz. There are also some generators that combine the functions of both AF and RF. This is another reason for knowing in which bands you anticipate working before you choose your generator. This flexibility of a generator to operate within several groups of frequencies will be discussed in the segment on waveforms.

If the hobbyist plans to do all his work within the audio range, he has no need to buy a generator which will soar far above that spectrum. However, the radio and TV repair technician will be working on audio amplifiers as well as RF receivers of various types. So, he must plan either to buy two generators, if he is busy enough, or one which will encompass all of the ranges in which he will work.

### RADIO FREQUENCY

Radio signals in their pure form are not transmitted by radio stations to the home radio or TV receiver. The information in the audio signal must be contained within an RF "envelope." What this means is that the audio frequency varies the radio frequency in some manner in a direct ratio to the energy contained in the audio signal. This is known as modulation. To modulate a signal is to vary either the amplitude, as it is done in the case of AM radio, or the frequency, as in FM and TV. Therefore an RF signal generator, when signal tracing or troubleshooting radios or TV sets, must be able to modulate the RF signal just as the radio transmitter does. If you look at the illustration in Fig. 1-39, you will see the audio frequency signal varying in degree of energy, the peaks representing the maximum energy contained in the signal and the dips the minimum energy. The RF content is represented by the filled-in section. A radio transmitter combines the two signals as shown in Fig. 1-40. The RF signal changes in amplitude by values determined by the amount of energy contained in the audio signal. What the AM radio receiver does

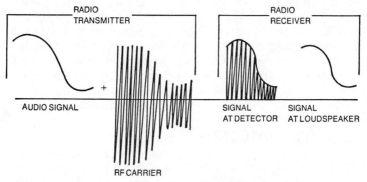

Fig. 1-39 Amplitude modulated signal.

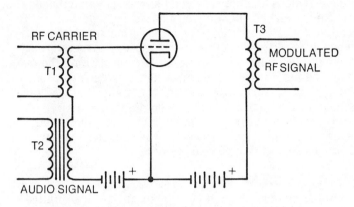

RF CARRIER

T1

T3

MODULATED
RF SIGNAL

T2

AUDIO SIGNAL

T2, T3—RF TRANSFORMERS
T2—AN IRON-CORE TRANSFORMER

Fig. 1-40. RF modulating stage at radio station.

is to reverse the process. The RF signal is removed, leaving only the audio signal, which is the only part we can hear.

FM differs from AM in two respects: (1) the range of frequencies differ; (2) the amplitude of the FM carrier wave remains constant while its frequency is varied by the instantaneous value of the modulating signal. Fig. 1-41 shows how the radio frequency varies depending on the instantaneous amplitude of the audio modulation.

A modulated RF signal generator must combine an RF oscillator circuit as well as an AF oscillator. The two waveforms are combined to produce the modulated waveform which is used for testing. However, as you can understand from the previous explanation, an FM signal generator cannot be substituted for an AM, or standard RF generator. Then too, specialized generators are used for work on FM stereo since they must generate two distinct FM signals of two frequencies.

With AM stereo advocates making noises for it to be heard as a transmitting medium, we will soon need an AM multiplex generator. However, it will be several years before the first AM stereo broadcast will be heard and the first receiving set bought. By that time, test instrument manufacturers will be turning out generators able to troubleshoot these sets.

## GENERATOR DISTORTION

Whether we are employing a sine or square wave for testing, we tend to believe that if we have a decent scope and an adequate signal generator, we have a perfect waveform against which we can compare the output of an amplifier or some such circuit. Is this necessarily true?

A square wave will show if there is much distortion in the basic waveform, as even a slight amount will result in imperfectly square corners which the eye easily recognizes. The sine wave's distortion is harder to see, as was pointed out previously. It has been suggested that a triangle wave is a better waveform for testing. But, if you have a sine wave generator and though it may seem pretty good to you, one can never be sure how much distortion exists in its output. The manufacturer's manual specifies the figure, but that was true only when the generator was new. No matter how expensive your equipment, as it ages the components will change their value.

The other solution is to find out what the percentage of distortion is at present. In the lab, the percentage of inherent distortion is known and is deducted from any results obtained with that unit. However, for the hobbyist that solution is not practical. The piece of sophisticated equipment used to determine the degree of distortion costs more than the average generator. All is not lost however; there is a solution to the problem.

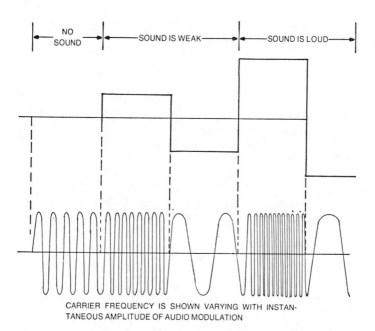

CARRIER FREQUENCY IS SHOWN VARYING WITH INSTAN-
TANEOUS AMPLITUDE OF AUDIO MODULATION

Fig. 1-41. Frequency modulated signal.

# DIFFERENTIATION.*

To differentiate a waveform is to pass it through an R-C network such as is basically shown in Fig. 1-42. With such a combination of resistor and capacitor placed between the output of a generator and the input of a scope, a square wave will come out as a spike waveform—this type of wave is often used in pulse generators. The sine wave will also show some distortion (but less so) because the sine wave is basically a pure tone and the differentiation affects the harmonics more than the fundamental tone. A differentiating network produces an output voltage which is proportional to the rate of change to the input voltage, and the output waveform is out of phase with the input, leading it by 90 degrees. With differentiation, we are able to know how much distortion exists in the basic waveform, but more importantly, even 1 or 2% distortion in the output of an amplifier becomes obvious.

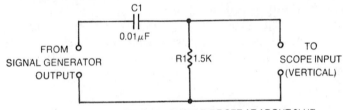

GENERATOR'S FREQUENCY SHOULD BE SET AT ABOUT 3kHZ
C1—0.01μF TUBULAR PAPER CAPACITOR
R1—1500 OHM CARBON RESISTOR

Fig. 1-42. Differentiating circuit.

The circuit shown in Fig. 1-43 is based on the principle explained. In this circuit, we use an op amp inverter with a capacitor input, this forming the differentiator. Potentiometer R1 is used to adjust the high-frequency response, while R3 and C3 (optional) remove any AC voltage present in the non-inverting input of the op amp. If R3 and C3 are left out, the + input of the op amp should be grounded. C2 is used only if very low noise operation is wanted. The high frequency cutoff point can be calculated from the equation:

$$F_0 = \frac{1}{6.28(R_1 C_1)}$$

For low frequency cutoff:

---

*Thanks to Leslie Solomon, Technical Editor of *Popular Electronics Magazine* for permission to use this material as well as his op amp circuit.

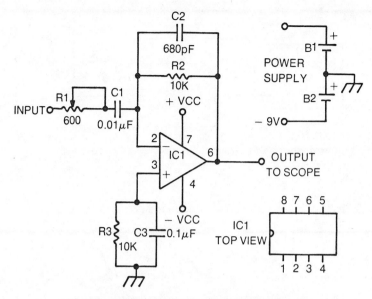

B1, B2—9-VOLT TRANSISTOR RADIO BATTERY
C1—0.01μF DISC CERAMIC CAPACITOR
C2—680pF SILVER MACA CAPACITOR
C3—0.1μF MYLAR TUBULAR CAPACITOR
R1—600 OHM LINEAR TAPER POTENTIOMETER
R2, R3—10,000 OHM CARBON RESISTOR
IC1—741 OP AMP (RADIO SHACK 276-010, OR EQUAL)

Fig. 1-43. IC differentiator.

$$F_1 = \frac{1}{6.28(R_2C_1)}$$

For the lowest noise, $R_1C_1$ should equal $R_2C_2$.

To see the results of differentiation, first produce a one or two-hertz waveform from the audio sine wave generator on the CRT. With a dual trace oscilloscope, you can view the output from the generator at the same time you view the results when the wave has been differentiated. Without that feature on the scope, us the setup shown in Fig. 1-44. Adjustment of R1 will emphasize the distortion. The experimenter may want to try differentiating a square wave and a triangle. The results are surprising.

## SPECIALIZED SIGNAL GENERATORS

There are many signal generators whose uses are so highly specialized that they are generally only known and understood by a relatively few workers in the field. For

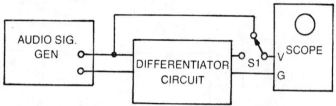

SWITCH S1 IS USED TO COMPARE A SINE WAVE BEFORE AND AFTER DIFFERENTIATION. SCOPE TRACES BELOW SHOW TYPICAL RESULTS.

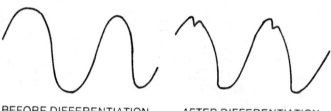

BEFORE DIFFERENTIATION    AFTER DIFFERENTIATION

Fig. 1-44. Observing distortion in a sine wave.

example, there are sweep and marker generators designed for aligning color and black and white TV sets and FM receivers; color generators which provide color signals with gated color burst for servicing color TV; grid-dip meters for tuning ham equipment, and many others.

Only two of the more specialized types will be discussed below, either because of their simplicity and maybe the experimenter might try his hand at them (as in the case of the white noise generator), or because it is a tool which can be of use of most hobbyists and technicians.

### Noise Generator

A noise generator occupies an unusual place on the workbench. Noise is usually an unwanted source of random energy with a highly complex waveform. Noise characteristically will have equal energy over a wide frequency band. But, while it is the very thing that should not appear in high fidelity circuits whether AM, FM, or TV, strangely enough it does have its uses for test purposes.

The circuit shown in Fig. 1-45 is a "white" noise generator used to align a shortwave receiver. As is apparent from studying the circuit, the diode is reversed. By this reverse biasing, white noise is generated. The output impedence is roughly the value of R3, which is 50 ohms.

Experimenters have used the white noise circuits to get a sound which closely imitates the "whooshing" of the surf (dentists have fed the output of the generator to an amplifier to calm a nervous patient). Such generators have also been used to induce sleep, as this type of sound seems to produce a calming effect on the nerves.

## Generator and Signal Tracer

Some signal generators, whether AF or RF, combine a signal tracer within the same chassis. These are used in troubleshooting radio receivers and audio equipment. In essence, the incorporated tracer is an amplifier with an output terminated with a small loudspeaker. If the signal is connected to a low level input, there might be no audible signal being produced if the circuit being tested is unable to amplify sufficiently a signal so minute. For example, the signal tracing section of the generator could be connected to the low level output of a preamplifier. Since this signal tracer has its own amplifier, it would then further amplify the sound from the circuit under test and amplify within its own circuit and feed it to its own loudspeaker.

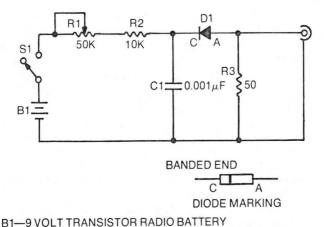

B1—9 VOLT TRANSISTOR RADIO BATTERY
C1—0.001 $\mu$F DISC CERAMIC CAPACITOR
D1—ALMOST ANY DIODE MAY BE USED. WITH SOME, R2 MAY NEED TO BE CHANGED.
R1—50,000 OHM AUDIO TAPER POTENTIOMETER
R2—10,000 OHM CARBON RESISTOR
R3—50 OHM CARBON RESISTOR
S1—SINGLE-POLE, SINGLE-THROW SWITCH

Fig. 1-45. White noise generator.

What is being done actually is substituting another amplifier and loudspeaker for the ones in the circuit which are suspect. Substitution, whether it be an amplifier, loudspeaker or a single component, is a very fast way of determining where the problem lies in a non-working or partially-working circuit. This method spotlights the source of the trouble almost at once. An amplifier might be fully operative, but the loudspeaker wires have come loose from the loudspeaker. The signal tracer will point this out. By using the signal tracer at one end, the output of the circuit under test and the signal generator at the input, the defective stage can quickly be located. Then, it is a matter of finding which component is guilty. From several hundred components in an amplifier, the problem is now limited to finding which of a dozen components are shorted, open-ended, or simply not working as they should.

Specialized generators, like any other specialized equipment, come into being to serve a particular need. However, the equipment is not necessarily complex.

## SUMMARY

To summarize the qualities of a signal generator, here is a list of those most needed:

1. *Range*. If one is working in radio as well as in audio frequencies, then a signal generator must be able to provide all of these ranges. If, however, the bulk of the work is one group of frequencies, then there is no point in buying more than is needed. If there is the possibility that in the future more frequencies will be employed, it would be foolish to have to buy once again.

2. *Constant Output*. This is important when carrying out tests which involve measurements over several frequencies. A constant output assures you that the generator is capable of putting out the same output voltage in each band.

3. *Stability of frequency and amplitude*. It is exasperating to have a generator that varies in its output or in its waveforms as time passes. Once the generator is warmed up properly—this means about five minutes with a tube unit or about two for a solid state model—it should remain steady as a rock over all of its ranges.

4. *Waveforms*. This point is somewhat similar to Point 1. How many waveforms do you need? Would one be enough, or do you need all three?

5. *Attenuators*. Any commercially-built units will have a series of step-down attenuators. Whether the unit has step-down or continually variable attenuators, the unit must present the same output impedance regardless of the amount of attenuation. If the impedance varies, so will the numbers being introduced into the measurements.

6. *Distortion-free output*. This includes hum, noise and unwanted harmonics. This is an obvious point, but sometimes one forgets that the signal generator must have less distortion in its waveforms than the unit that is being tested. The technician working on a $1000 amplifier with negligible distortion must be careful that his generator is not introducing distortion of its own. The hobbyist whose circuits may contain up to 5% distortion can get along very well with a generator whose output distortion may run as high as 2%.

7. *Tuning controls*. These must show careful calibration and be grouped in such a way so that from a human engineering viewpoint they are easy to use, eliminating confusion.

The experimenter or technician with unlimited money at his disposal could choose the most expensive generator on the market, or several, if he chooses. Since few of us are in that fortunate state, it behooves one to select and buy only what is needed at the best quality affordable.

## CALIBRATING THE TEST INSTRUMENTS

It is a common mistake to believe that our meters, signal generators and scopes, because they are considered standard instruments, are necessarily accurate. While it is true that an instrument that has been accurately built will give excellent results, it should not be forgotten that as the instrument ages, the components change value and consequently will be far from what they should be. This aging process is often unnoticeable and the errors due to this gradual change in values increase unbeknownst to the user. Therefore, it is a good idea to check these instruments periodically.

It may seem strange to see the signal generator being used to check the scope and the scope being used to check the generator. Which is first—the chicken or the egg? As long as it is known which instrument is right up to the mark, it can be used as the standard by which the others will be compared. If in doubt about all of them, and it is impossible to borrow a generator or VTVM you know to be accurate, remember the frequency of the house current is 60 Hz and varies by less than 0.03%. However, the voltage may vary from 105 to 117 VAC, so that cannot be used to calibrate the scope's AC input. Instead, three fresh batteries delivering a precise 4.5 volts can be used for checking the DC voltage measurement.

Once the scope is acceptable as a standard, then the signal generator can be checked against it. If there is some means of knowing that the generator is accurate, then the scope can be checked against the output voltage of the generator. A frequency counter provides an answer as to whether the signal generator is "right on" in its frequency output.

# Chapter 2

# Commercial
# Generators Available

This chapter contains photographs and a brief description of generators of many types—from the simple signal tracer to the complex laboratory instruments. This list is by no means complete, but will allow the reader to see for himself the various controls and the features of these generators. The degree of sophistication shown by these various units usually bears a direct ratio to the price tag. The prices shown are those furnished by the respective companies at the time of writing.

Not every manufacturer of signal generators is represented in this grouping. The author admits that the choice was completely arbitrary and there are many other excellent units on the market as any reader will quickly see. However, those included here provide a good cross-section of what is available on the market.

Fig. 2-1 CONTINENTAL SPECIALTIES 3-way Function Generator, Design Mate 2. Frequency from 1 Hz to 100 kHz. Low-distortion sine wave, high-linearity triangle wave, fast-rise-time square wave. Five decade ranges, accurate to 5% of dial setting with variable 100mV to 10 volt P-P output and constant 600-ohm impedance. Price $69.95.

Fig. 2-2. CONTINENTAL SPECIALTIES Pulse Generator, Design Mate 4. Frequency range from 0.5 Hz to 5 MHz, with pulse width from 100 nsec to 1 sec in seven overlapping ranges. Symmetrical and asymmetrical pulses with continuous, manual one-shot and external trigger operation. External triggering to 10 MHz. 100 mV to 15V positive output with synchronous output gating. Price $124.95.

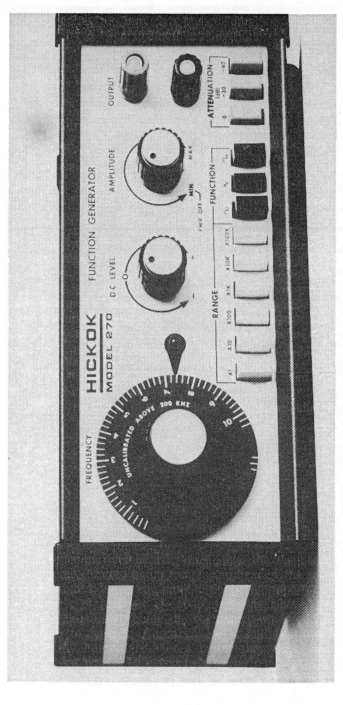

Fig. 2-3. HICKOK Function Generator. Model 270. Three waveforms from 1 Hz to 500 kHz in six ranges. With external connections. can produce logic pulses. sweeps and ramps. amplitude and frequency modulation outputs. phase and frequency shift keying signals. tone bursts and mixed signal outputs. Price $189.00.

75

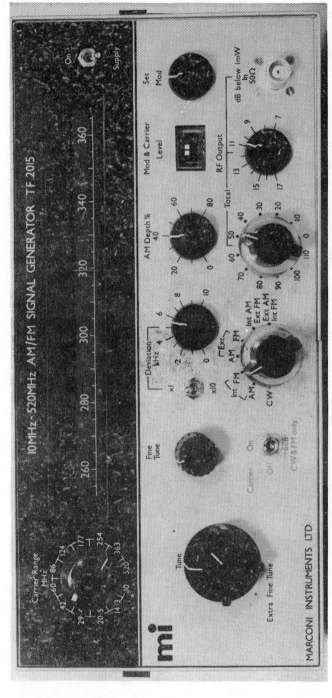

Fig. 2-4. MARCONI INSTRUMENTS AM/FM Signal Generator. Model TF 2015. Frequency from 10 to 520 MHz. Frequency modulation up to 100 kHz deviation. Amplitude modulation up to 80% depth. All solid state. portable. Used for testing mobile radio recievers including narrow-band UHF models. Automatic level control for good output accuracy. Eleven switched bands. each using voltage-tuned oscillators. Price $195.00.

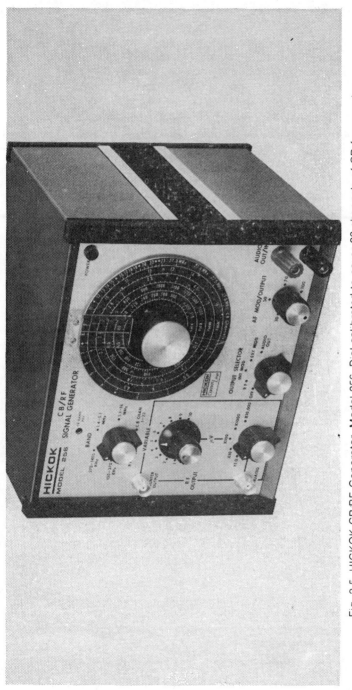

Fig. 2-5. HICKOK CB RF Generator. Model 256. Dial calibrated to cover 23 channels of CB frequencies. Overall frequencies from 100 kHz to 16 MHz in four bands. Adjustable internal modulation from 0 to 100°o. External modulation capability. Continuously variable calibrated and attenuated RF output up to 100V with 5-step position switch. Internal and external AM modulation and SSB modulation. Price $199.00.

77

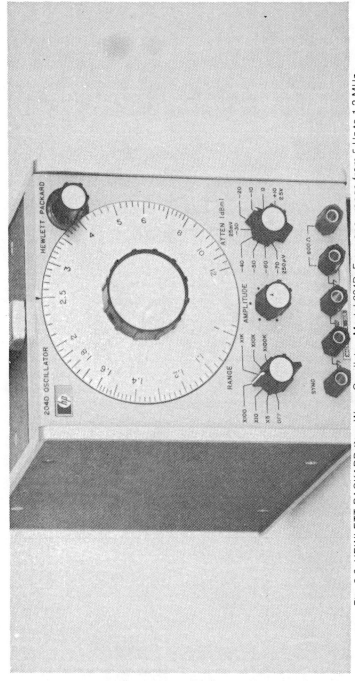

Fig. 2-6. HEWLETT-PACKARD Sine Wave Oscillator. Model 204D. Frequency range from 5 Hz to 1.2 MHz. with less than 0.1°. distortion between 30Hz and 100 kHz. Hum and noise less than 0.01°. of output. Output is from 2.5 V into 600 ohms down to 250 μV rms. Attenuator covers 80 dB range in 10 dB steps.with accuracy of ± 3°. Used for audio. medical and for low-level testing in ultrasonic apparatus. Price $325. AC operated. Optional battery operation. $340.

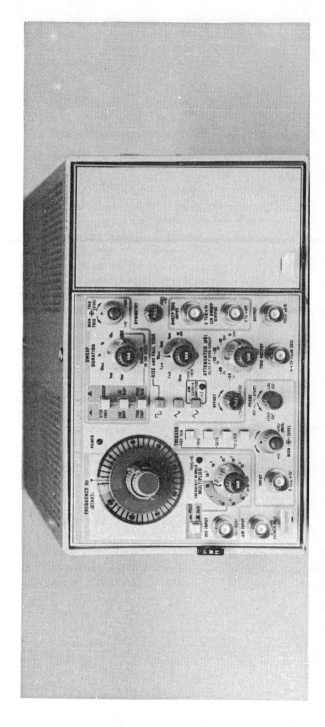

Fig. 2-7. TEKTRONIX 3-waveform Function Generator. Model FG 504. Frequency ranges from 0.001 Hz to mHz. logarithmic or linear sweep. Up to 30 volt P-P output. AM and FM with built-in attenuator. Phase lock mode with external and manual trigger or gate. Extra range of 20Hz to 20 kHz. for audio applications. can be plugged in. Price $1200.

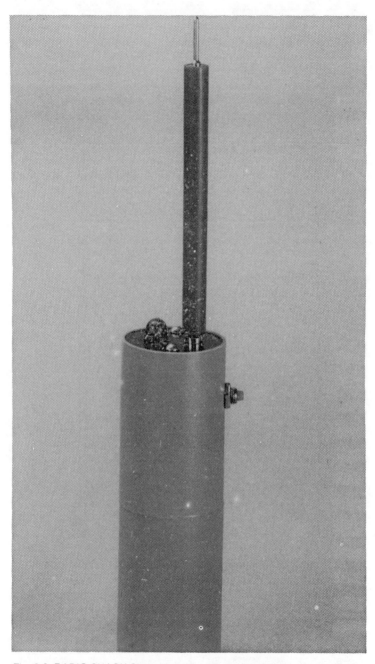

Fig. 2-8. RADIO SHACK Signal Injector, Model 22-4032. For RF, I-F and AF circuits. Pushbutton operation with battery-strength indicator lamp. Price $6.95.

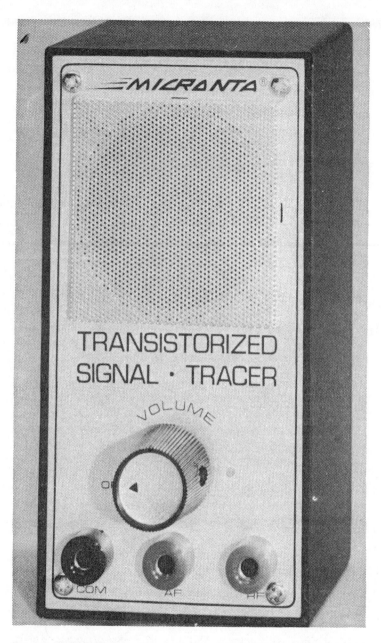

Fig. 2-9. MICRONTA Transistorized Signal Tracer. Checks RF, I-F and AF signals with built-in speaker. Operates on 9-volt battery. Made by Radio Shack. Price $12.95.

Fig. 2-10. HEATH RF Generator, Model IG-102. Source of modulated or un-modulated RF signals for AM, FM, TV, LW and SW broadcast bands. Frequency from 100 kHz to 100 MHz in 6 bands. 2% tuning accuracy. External modulation input; internal modulation is 400 Hz with 400 Hz audio output for audio testing. Price $44.95, wired only.

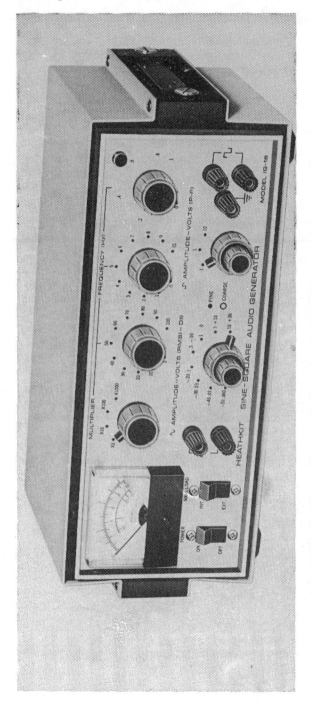

Fig. 2-11. HEATH Sine/Square Wave Audio Generator, Model IG-18. Sine wave frequency from 1 Hz to 100 kHz, with less than 0.1% distortion from 10 Hz to 20 kHz. Square wave from 5Hz to 100 kHz with P-P output levels of 0.1 and 10 volt into 2000 ohm load. Rise time is 50 nsecs. 3 range selectors and 3 multipliers. Vernier control for 0-1 range. Both waveforms available simultaneously. Price $84.95 kit, and $130.00 wired.

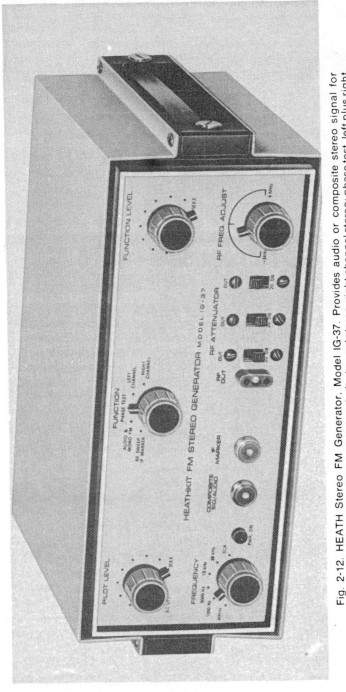

Fig. 2-12. HEATH Stereo FM Generator. Model IG-37. Provides audio or composite stereo signal for multiplex adjustments. FM modulation: Left channel stereo, right channel stereo: phase test, left plus right in phase. mono FM. Radio frequency 100 MHz ± 2 MHz. Crystal-controlled 19 kHz pilot signal for checking lock-in ranges. Built-in sweep and marker signals for RF and I-F alignment. Price $99.95 wired only.

Fig. 2-13. Sweep/Function Generator, Model 390. Frequency from 0.2 Hz to 200 kHz in four overlapping ranges. Linear or logarithmic sweep in three sweep rates and four frequency ranges. Distortion less than 1%. Attenuator from 0 to 62 dB in 10 dB increments. Variable output control 10 volt P-P on all three functions. Price $169.95 assembled.

Fig. 2-14. EICO Solid State Sine/Square Wave generator, Model 379. Sine wave frequency from 20 Hz to 2 MHz; square wave from 20 Hz to 200 kHz. Output 0 to 10 volt P-P. Calibration accuracy 3%, except from 5% for 20 Hz to 100 Hz and 1 MHz to 2 MHz ranges. Price $99.95 for kit and $129.95 for wired model.

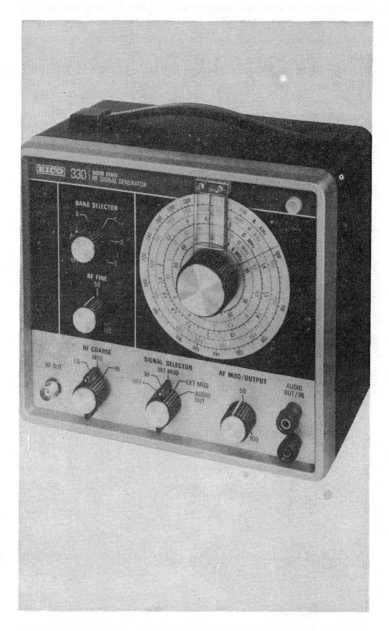

Fig. 2-15. EICO RF Signal Generator, Model 330. Fundamental frequencies from 100 kHz to 54 MHz in 5 bands. Internal 400 Hz signal available for testing audio equipment and to modulate all RF frequencies. Internal modulation from 0 to 100%. Output more than 300 millivolts into 50-ohm load. Price $79.95 kit, or $119.95 wired.

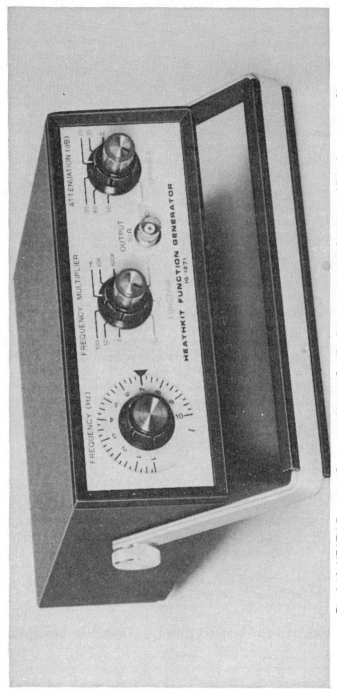

Fig. 2-16. HEATH Function Generator. Model IG-1271. Frequency range 0.1 Hz to 1 MHz. Accuracy ± 3%. Frequency control 100:1 range with 6-position multiplier. Triangle waveform non-linearity, 5% max., square waveform 100 nsec rise or fall time, sine waveform 3°₀ max from 5 Hz to 100 kHz. Signal 10 volt P-P into 50-ohm load. Price $99.95 kit, or $150.00 wired.

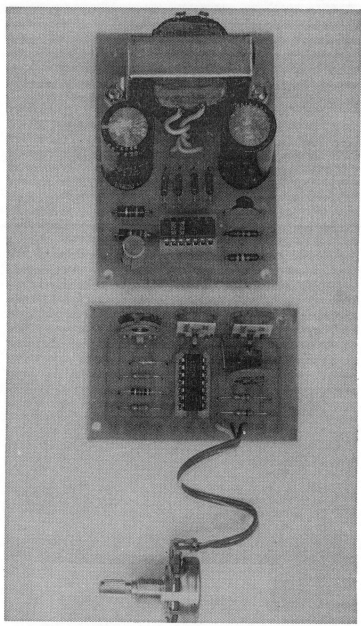

Fig. 2-17. PHOTOLUME CORP., 3-way Function Generator. Frequency range from 200 to 20 kHz with continuously variable control. Less than 5% distortion. All waveforms available simultaneously. Battery operated (9V) or 117 VAC with separate power supply. Price (kit) $10.95, not including power supply, shown above photo of generator.

# Chapter 3

# Knowing What

# Your Generator Can Do

Signal generators are like any other piece of test equipment—they have their capabilities and limitations. Therefore, when testing components, circuits, or systems—the test results will not only reflect the operating parameters of the item under test, but the inherent limitations (or defects) of the testing instrument. In other words, you can only get out of something what you put into it. Somehow, that sounds familiar, but nevertheless, it's true. Therefore, this chapter is devoted to methods for checking exactly what the particular AF or RF signal generator being employed is actually producing.

## CHECKING AN RF GENERATOR

Not all generators have equal output over their entire frequency range. This is particularly true with RF generators. But, because a generator output is not entirely "flat" is no reason for limiting its use to that of a doorstop. If one knows where it is not flat, this characteristic can be taken into consideration when taking readings. With the circuit shown, it becomes a simple matter to know where the generator can be depended on and where one must accept the readings with a grain of salt.

## Procedure

The generator in question is connected through an RF probe to the circuit in the illustration. To avoid erroneous readings, it is best to build the circuit inside a metal chassis—since we are dealing with RF ranges this precaution is necessary—or use a breadboard which is designed for RF. In either case, procure graph paper and mark the vertical axis in volts and the horizontal in frequency. The VTVM is now set to read low voltage. The generator is set to some output voltage that will give a reading on the VTVM. The frequency should be at the lowest range of the generator. Take a reading of the voltage shown on the VTVM at the frequency shown by the generator's dials. Mark that on the graph paper. Continue over the entire range of the generator. When enough points have been obtained, draw a line connecting them so that a curve results. Shown is a typical curve that might result.

**Checking an RF generator**

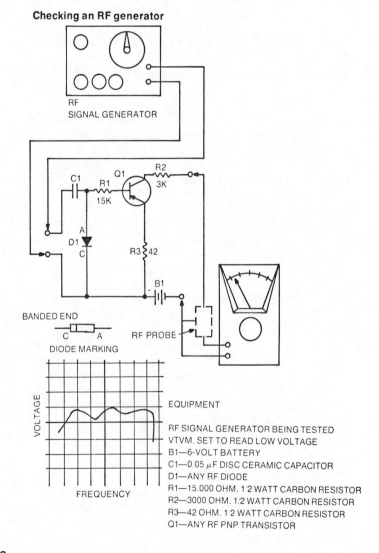

EQUIPMENT

RF SIGNAL GENERATOR BEING TESTED
VTVM. SET TO READ LOW VOLTAGE
B1—6-VOLT BATTERY
C1—0.05 μF DISC CERAMIC CAPACITOR
D1—ANY RF DIODE
R1—15.000 OHM. 1/2 WATT CARBON RESISTOR
R2—3000 OHM. 1/2 WATT CARBON RESISTOR
R3—42 OHM. 1/2 WATT CARBON RESISTOR
Q1—ANY RF PNP TRANSISTOR

## CHECKING ACCURACY

To obtain meaningful measurements, all of the instruments must be of guaranteed accuracy. It should not be forgotten that it can happen that an RF generator is putting out a frequency different from the dial settings. The output level

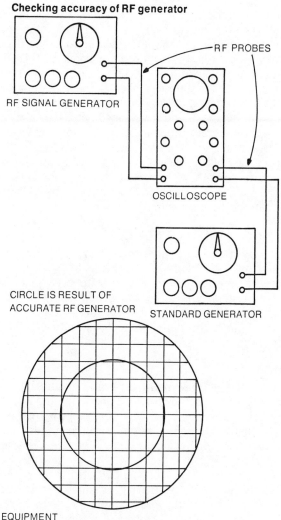

**Checking accuracy of RF generator**

RF PROBES

RF SIGNAL GENERATOR

OSCILLOSCOPE

CIRCLE IS RESULT OF
ACCURATE RF GENERATOR

STANDARD GENERATOR

EQUIPMENT
RF GENERATOR BEING CHECKED
OSCILLOSCOPE. SET TO PRODUCE LISSAJOUS FIGURES
STANDARD GENERATOR, CONNECTED TO H INPUTS OF
SCOPE
VTVM OF KNOWN ACCURACY

can also vary from the meter reading. So, it is worth the time spent to have one of the instruments checked against a known standard. In this case, let us presume that the scope and the VTVM are accurate. We can then quickly find if the generator is also producing what it should.

### Procedure

Check the accuracy of the frequency as put out by the generator with the set up below. Another generator known to be accurate is connected to the horizontal inputs of the scope. The vertical inputs go to the generator under test. Begin with the lowest band, for example, 100 kHz. The standard is also set to that frequency. If the generator is accurate, a stationary circle will be produced on the scope's screen. Repeat this test at one or more points of each frequency band.

To check the maximum output voltage level, the generator is connected to an accurate VTVM by means of an RF probe. See that as the voltage level is reduced the action, as seen on the meter, is smooth with no sudden fits. Any variances in either frequency or output level should be adjusted as described in the owner's manual.

### CHECKING THE OUTPUT VOLTAGE

Since any measurement is dependent on the accuracy of the measuring instruments, it is basic to know their limits. A signal generator is subject to the limits imposed on it due to its design. As it gets older, the tubes and the other assorted components will change values. The arrangement shown is designed to check the uniformity of the output voltage of a generator over all of its frequency ranges.

### Procedure

Connect the output signal generator to the input of the scope through a load resistor. This resistor must match the output impedance of the generator. The scope is set to read AC volts. The horizontal gain is reduced so the trace is merely a straight vertical line, the waveshape being of no interest. Output voltages are plotted on as many points along the frequency range as possible. The output, if in the RF range, should be checked with an RF probe which is substituted for the direct probe used in the audio range.

The graph is merely shown as a sample and does not represent any particular generator. What it is meant to suggest is that the more points that are plotted, the better will the resulting curve and represent the true picture of the signal generator's output.

**Checking generator's output voltage**

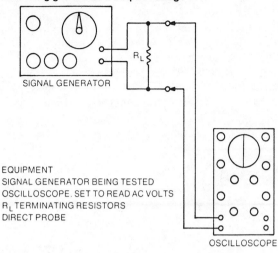

EQUIPMENT
SIGNAL GENERATOR BEING TESTED
OSCILLOSCOPE. SET TO READ AC VOLTS
R$_L$ TERMINATING RESISTORS
DIRECT PROBE

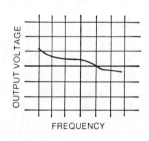

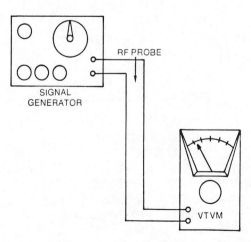

95

## CALIBRATING THE VOLTAGE SCALE

When determining the voltage gains of an amplifier, the accuracy of the output of the generator is relatively unimportant since only a ratio is involved. When exact measurements are being made and the generator's output is varied over several of its scales, then one must know the precise output voltage. The set-up described furnishes a simple way of calibrating the generator very accurately.

**Checking generator's voltage scale**

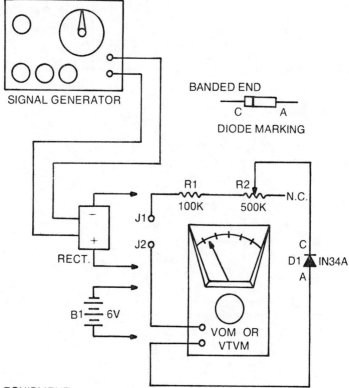

EQUIPMENT
SIGNAL GENERATOR
FULL WAVE BRIDGE RECTIFIER
B1—BATTERIES TOTALING 6 VOLTS
VOM, SET TO READ μA (OR A 50 μA METER MAY BE SUBSTITUTED)
R1—100,000 OHM, 1/2 WAT CARBON RESISTOR
R2—500,000 OHM LINEAR POTENTIOMETER
D1—IN43A DIODE (RADIO SHACK 276)

## Procedure

Four fresh batteries are used in series to obtain exactly six volts. They can be of the C or D type. As long as the test is not extended too long, the batteries will show no appreciable voltage drop. The circuit uses a potentiometer to limit the current which is metered by M1. A VTVM set for a low DC reading can also be used. The drop across the diode, D1, is exactly 0.1 volt when the current is reduced to 20 $\mu$A.

Without touching the setting of the pot, the square wave generator is substituted for the batteries. Adjust the generator's output so the meter reads exactly 6 volts. If the generator's scale is off, the unit should be adjusted internally.

## MEASURING PERCENTAGE OF MODULATION

The degree or percentage of modulation from the output of the signal generator modulator should be measured when

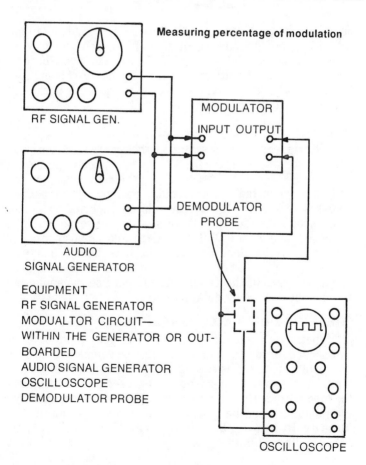

**Measuring percentage of modulation**

RF SIGNAL GEN.

MODULATOR
INPUT OUTPUT

AUDIO
SIGNAL GENERATOR

DEMODULATOR
PROBE

EQUIPMENT
RF SIGNAL GENERATOR
MODUALTOR CIRCUIT—
WITHIN THE GENERATOR OR OUT-
BOARDED
AUDIO SIGNAL GENERATOR
OSCILLOSCOPE
DEMODULATOR PROBE

OSCILLOSCOPE

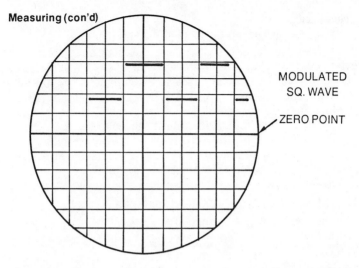

MODULATED
SQ. WAVE

ZERO POINT

doing checks on a receiver. Receivers are usually examined with 85% modulation and it is a good idea to know the percentage of modulation existing. This percentage is based on the relative output voltages of the two generators being used. A modulator is 100% modulated when the negative peak of the square wave touches the zero-volt level.

**Procedure**

With a frequency generated by the square wave generator (which is below the upper limit of the demodulator probe) and with the RF generator set to any convenient frequency, both units are connected to the modulator's input. The modulator output is passed through a demodulator probe and terminated by the scope's vertical inputs. By shorting the scope terminals, the base line appears. With the short removed, a square wave will be observed floating above the base line. A dual-trace scope would permit both traces to show as in the sketch. The output voltages of the generators can now be manipulated to achieve the desired modulation.

**CHECKING MODULATOR LINEARITY**

Whether an integral part of an rf generator, or as an outboarded circuit, a modulator must be completely linear or the results will be misleading. Is the distortion appearing on the CRT due to the receiver being checked or is it the fault of the modulator? By using the test setup shown, the linearity of the modulator can be quickly shown, as well as its range of linearity. By knowing the latter, you avoid using the modulator above its linear limits.

## Procedure

The output of the audio square wave generator and that of the rf generator are connected together and then fed to the input of the modulator circuit. In cases when the modulator is built within the RF generator, then the audio connections must be attached to the output of the RF generator. When the modulator is outboarded, then follow the arrangement in the illustration. S1 switch permits viewing the trace directly from the audio generator and then by switching to its other position, you obtain the effect of the modulator—if any. As you can see, both scope traces should be similar. Although there is bound to exist some discrepancies, this should be noted so that the effect of the modulator on a circuit being tested is known. If the scope is a dual-trace unit, S1 becomes unnecessary since both outputs—before and after modulation—can be viewed simultaneously.

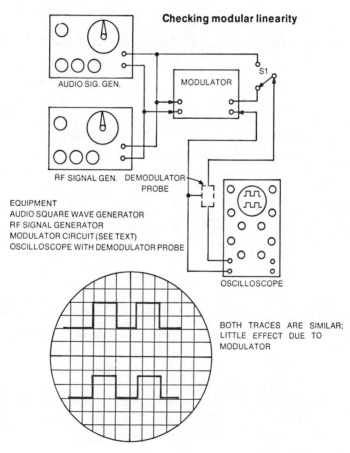

**Checking modular linearity**

AUDIO SIG. GEN.

MODULATOR

S1

RF SIGNAL GEN.     DEMODULATOR PROBE

EQUIPMENT
AUDIO SQUARE WAVE GENERATOR
RF SIGNAL GENERATOR
MODULATOR CIRCUIT (SEE TEXT)
OSCILLOSCOPE WITH DEMODULATOR PROBE

OSCILLOSCOPE

BOTH TRACES ARE SIMILAR; LITTLE EFFECT DUE TO MODULATOR

## IMPEDANCE MATCHING PADS

A square wave generator may produce excellent waveforms with good rise times, but if the impedance of the circuit to which the generator is connected does not match that of the generator the results will be less than perfect. The simple gadget shown below consists of three matching pads to avoid this trouble. They will provide the proper termination for the 50-ohm coaxial cable from the generator.

### Procedure

The pads are built inside a small metal box. P1 and P2 are banana plugs which fit right into the jacks of the generator. Obviously if your unit has different terminals then use plugs which will match. Solder a length of coaxial cable from the output of the case terminating with a probe for J1 and an alligator clip for J2. The switch, S1, permits you to select three different impedances to match the impedances of the circuit under test.

Position 1—results in a 72-ohm impedance
Position 2—results in a 300 ohm inpedance
Position 3—results in a 300 ohm balanced input

Due to the completely resistive quality of the circuit there will be a certain percentage of signal loss.

**Impedance matching pads**

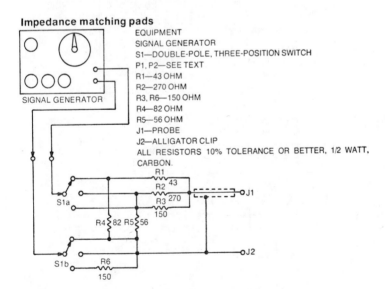

EQUIPMENT
SIGNAL GENERATOR
S1—DOUBLE-POLE, THREE-POSITION SWITCH
P1, P2—SEE TEXT
R1—43 OHM
R2—270 OHM
R3, R6—150 OHM
R4—82 OHM
R5—56 OHM
J1—PROBE
J2—ALLIGATOR CLIP
ALL RESISTORS 10% TOLERANCE OR BETTER, 1/2 WATT, CARBON.

# Chapter 4

# Checking
# Other Instruments

Now that we know what a signal generator is and how it is to be used—let's put it to work. First, as the generator is only one of the primary pieces of test equipment in the electronics shop, it can be used to check for proper operation of the other instruments. This chapter provides calibration procedures and checks which enables you to know exactly what your oscilloscope, probes, and VTVM are capable of.

## CALIBRATING A SCOPE VERTICAL AMPLIFIER

A signal generator makes calibration of a scope a simple operation. A scope that is voltage calibrated permits troubleshooting TV and audio equipment, since one can obtain a waveform and a voltage reading at the same time.

The deflection sensitivity of a scope is expressed as in the number of volts required at the input terminal to produce a trace one inch high, with the vertical amplifier set at maximum. A service scope's sensitivity may be expressed as 25-millivolt per inch. This means that only .0.025 volt is required to deflect the trace by one inch. If the scope's V amplifier is linear, 4 times that voltage will produce a 4-inch trace.

## Procedure

With the instruments connected as shown, the signal generator may be tuned within any frequency within the range of the scope. Any frequency within that range with a one-volt output will serve. Peak-to-peak voltages are more useful than

**Calibrating scopes vertical amplifier**

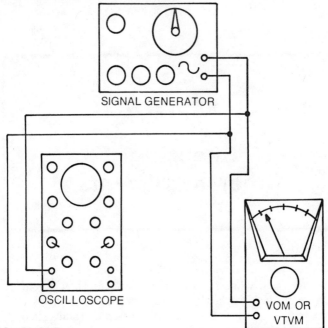

SIGNAL GENERATOR

OSCILLOSCOPE

VOM OR
VTVM

EQUIPMENT

SIGNAL GENERATOR, SET TO PRODUCE A TRACE WITHIN
THE SCOPE'S FREQUENCY RANGE
OSCILLOSCOPE BEING CALIBRATED
VTVM, SET TO READ AC VOLTAGES

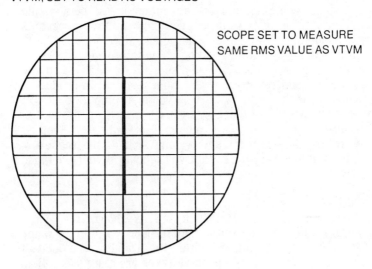

SCOPE SET TO MEASURE
SAME RMS VALUE AS VTVM

rms. but if the VTVM is calibrated in rms, then multiply the indicated rms values by 2.83.

Set the scope's controls as follows:

1. Vertical attenuator at maximum gain
2. Sweep frequency to match the generator's
3. Vertical fine control to maximum
4. Horizontal gain to minimum (to obtain a straight line)

The attenuator on the generator should be set to give the maximum height on the distortionless area of the screen. Center the trace. Set the scale of the VTVM so that the reading is as close to full scale as possible. Use a grease pencil (also called a china marker) to draw a straight line from top to bottom of the trace. The bottom point is marked ZERO and the top with the full scale voltage. Divide the scale into equal parts with their values in volts. The attenuator control is set to the next range and the output from the generator is reduced to provide a trace the same height as the previous one. Values are written in. The same method is used to calibrate each setting of the attenuator. With this information on the screen, voltages can be read as the wave forms are studied.

## CHECKING LINEARITY OF A
## SCOPE VERTICAL AMPLIFIER

A fault sometimes encountered, although its source is rarely recognized, is the non-linearity of the vertical amplifier of an oscilloscope. The result is blamed usually on the signal generator or the circuit under test, with the fault appearing as an asymmetrical tilt of the square wave. While it is normal for tilting at low frequencies, the square wave will tilt symmetrically, that is, the upper part of the trace showing as much tilt as the lower. This effect is due to attenuation and phase shift. But, when asymmetrical tilting is observed—then a problem exists. The test shown here will quickly put the blame for the asymmetrical tilt where it properly belongs.

### Procedure

Connect the equipment as shown in the accompanying illustration. Begin with a low frequency square wave and observe the trace. Make certain that the wave is as square as the generator is capable of producing. If possible, try to get a 50% duty cycle; it makes it easier to judge faults. An ideal waveform is with the upper and lower part of the trace having the same length. Tune the generator upwards to 1 kHz and then move up to 10 kHz, while observing the scope trace for signs of

103

tilt. Continue tuning upward. When up above 20 kHz, be sure to use an RF probe. If the tilt at each frequency range is seen to be unsymmetrical, and if the generator is known from a previous test on another scope, that it is capable of producing a near perfect trace, then the fault of the unsymmetrical tilt is obviously due to the vertical amplifier of the scope. In that case, the first thing to be done is to check the tubes in that part of the circuit.

**Checking linearity of scope's v-amplifier**

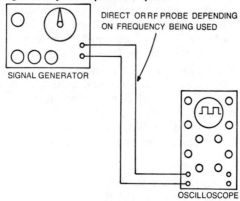

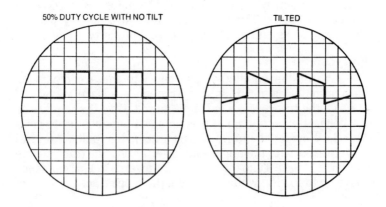

## CALIBRATING A DOUBLE-ENDED SCOPE

In most cases the oscilloscope is used as a single-ended instrument; that is, both vertical input terminals are tied together by a cable or a metal jumper connector. But, there are times when the circuit does not allow grounding one side, such as in audio output tests, when the scope must be used as a double-ended instrument. When this is done, however, the scope must be calibrated for that purpose. This is easily done with a signal generator. The output meter on the generator indicates a precise AC voltage which is used for calibration in this test.

### Procedure

First, remove the jumper connector between the two vertical inputs. The scope case should be grounded to the chassis of the signal generator. The sine wave output of the generator is then set for any convenient frequency within the range of the scope. First, with switch S1 in position 1, measure the voltage between the first vertical input of the scope and the ground point. Add to that the voltage as measured between vertical input 2 and ground. The sum of the two voltages is the calibrating voltage. It is understood that the output voltage from the generator is not varied during the test.

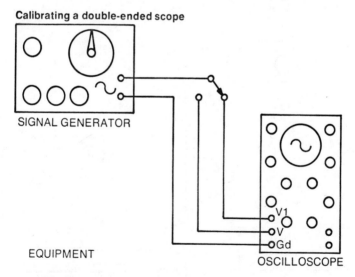

Calibrating a double-ended scope

SIGNAL GENERATOR

V1

V

Gd

EQUIPMENT

OSCILLOSCOPE

AUDIO SINE WAVE GENERATOR
SCOPE, WITH CONNECTOR BETWEEN
V2 AND GROUND REMOVED

## CHECKING A SCOPE'S AC AND DC RESPONSE

An oscilloscope in good working condition should offer exactly equal deflections whether the input voltage is DC or AC, as long as the voltage is equal in both cases. Even if originally the scope had that quality, with age the conditions change. It is worthwhile—this test takes only minutes—to know if the response is unequal and therefore resulting in inaccurate measurements.

### Procedure

A signal generator is set to some frequency—its actual value is unimportant. The output voltage must be set very accurately so that it matches the voltage from a known to be accurate source of DC voltage. The voltage in both units must be equal. This is important. The height of the DC deflection, such as shown in the illustration, must be equal to the top of the trace resulting from the voltage produced by the signal generator. If they are not, the oscilloscope is at fault. Whether minor differences can be tolerated depends on how accurate your measurements must be.

Checking scope's AC & DC response

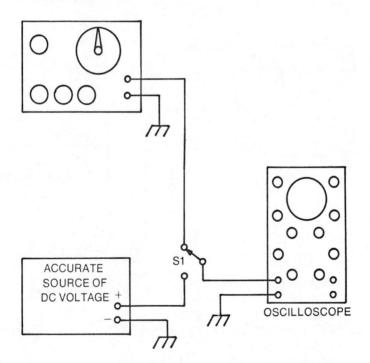

EQUIPMENT
SIGNAL GENERATOR
ACCURATE SOURCE OF DC VOLTAGE
S1—SINGLE-POLE, SINGLE-THROW
OSCILLOSCOPE BEING TESTED

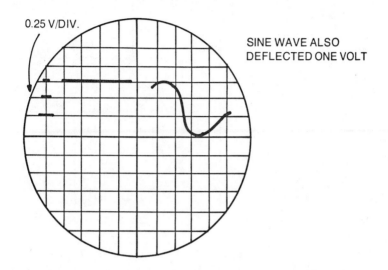

0.25 V/DIV.

SINE WAVE ALSO
DEFLECTED ONE VOLT

## CHECKING THE OSCILLOSCOPE FOR ASTIGMATISM

Astigmatism causes a scope to exhibit a trace which is in focus only in parts. Regardless of the manipulation of the focusing control, sections of the trace remain out of focus. This can suggest distortion in a circuit being checked when actually the oscilloscope is at fault. This is one of the many tests to enable you to determine if your testing equipment is operating as it should.

### Procedure

The output of the signal generator is connected directly to the vertical input of the scope, as well as to the horizontal input. The generator is set for a 60 Hz sine wave. The sync sweep is set to "Horizontal 600 Hz." The vertical control is turned to obtain an ellipse large enough to be studied. See the illustration. Turn the phasing control so that the ellipse is as large as possible. Now focus the trace very carefully. If all the edges are smooth there is no astigmatism. If astigmatism is present it will show up with out-of-focus sections as illustrated. The fault will be most prevalent usually either at the top and bottom or on the sides of the CRT.

**Checking the oscilloscope for astigmatism**

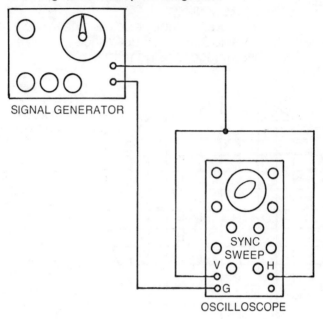

SIGNAL GENERATOR

OSCILLOSCOPE

EQUIPMENT

SIGNAL GENERATOR, SET AT 60 Hz
OSCILLOSCOPE BEING CHECKED

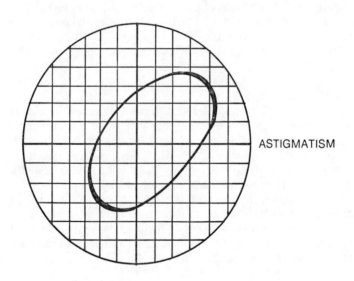

ASTIGMATISM

# DETERMINING INPUT RESISTANCE OF A SCOPE

Knowing a scope's input resistance is important for various measurements where this resistance may need to be calculated into the result. Every owner's manual contains this information, but if the manual is lost—all is not lost. With a signal generator and a potentiometer, the input resistance is quickly measured.

## Procedure

Connect a sine wave generator as shown in the sketch, with switch S1 in position 1. Set the output of the generator so the signal level can be easily measured with a 60 or 100 Hz tone Let us say that the signal covers four divisions on the scope screen with the vertical attenuator set so the measurement equals four volts. The actual height of the trace is unimportant, just so it can be easily read. Without touching any of the controls, flip switch to position 2. Adjust the pot so the wave is exactly half of its previous height. In our example the trace would then cover only two divisions. Remove the pot from the circuit and carefully measure that part of the resistance which was introduced into the circuit. That resistance, usually in megohms, is the input resistance of the scope.

**Determining input resistance of scope**

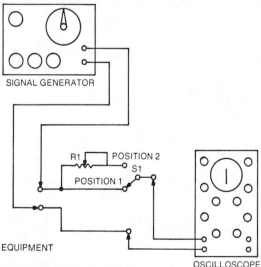

AUDIO SIGNAL GENERATOR
R1—10 MEGOHM LINEAR TAPER POTENTIOMETER
S1—SINGLE-POLE, DOUBLE-THROW
OSCILLOSCOPE BEING MEASURED

## CHECKING FOR CROSS-TALK
## WITHIN A SCOPE'S AMPLIFIERS

Cross-talk is not limited to the effects of signals existing between two channels of a tape recorder. It can also make itself known between the horizontal and vertical amplifiers of a scope. The test is simple and requires only the time needed to warm up the scope and the signal generator.

### Procedure

Tune a square wave generator to any frequency within the limits of the scope. Obviously, the scope must be set to read that frequency. Connect the leads of the generator to the vertical amplifier terminals of the scope as in the illustration. Adjust the vertical gain to maximum and the horizontal gain to minimum. A single vertical line should result if there is no cross-talk. The scope picture illustrated shows the ideal result. If there is appreciable cross-talk, two parallel lines will show up, and these lines cannot be brought together by any manipulation of the controls. For the other part of the test, reconnect the leads of the generator to the horizontal as well as to the vertical terminals. The horizontal gain is set to maximum with no gain for the vertical amplifier. This is exactly the reverse of the settings for the previous test. This time, a single horizontal line should result if all is right. The drawing shows what you should expect if no cross-talk is present in your scope. Again, two lines will show on the CRT, but this time they will be horizontal.

Checking for cross-talk in scope's amplifiers

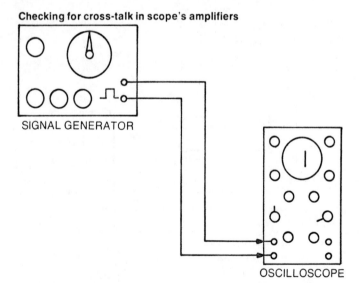

SIGNAL GENERATOR

OSCILLOSCOPE

EQUIPMENT

SIGNAL GENERATOR
OSCILLOSCOPE BEING TESTED

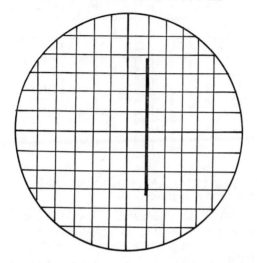

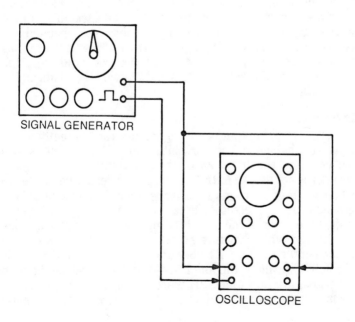

SIGNAL GENERATOR

OSCILLOSCOPE

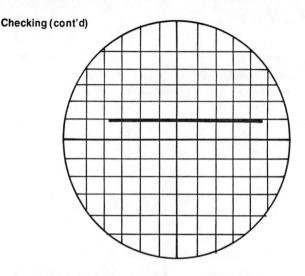

## CHECKING VERTICAL AND HORIZONTAL AMPLIFIERS OF A SCOPE

It is important to periodically check the horizontal and vertical amplifiers of an an oscilloscope. Due to tube aging, or that of other components causing changing values non-linearity of the amplifiers may result. This means that it becomes difficult to obtain meaningful results when using Lissajous figures on the scope. It is always dangerous to presume the accuracy on the part of any test instrument without this occasional checking. As has been pointed out before, any instrument used for measuring must be as accurate as possible. If it is off because of design, the "off-ness" should be known to avoid blaming the faults on the circuits being tested.

### Procedure

Connect the output of the signal generator directly to the inputs of the scope The horizontal input of the scope is also connected to the hot lead of the generator. The horizontal selector is set to EXTERNAL. The ground lead is connected to either the V or H ground (which one is unimportant, since both grounds are connected internally to the case of the scope). Adjust the gains of the V and H amplifiers until a straight line is obtained which crosses exactly at the graticule zero—the exact center of the CRT. See the illustration. If the line is absolutely straight, the amplifiers are linear and can be used for phase measurements. If there is a bend to the line, or a "blob" exists, as in the illustration, linearity exists and phase measurements will be affected to some degree. The linearity can be restored by having the instrument checked by an experienced technician. Voltages inside the scope are high enough to be lethal. So be careful!

**Checking V and H amplifiers of scope**

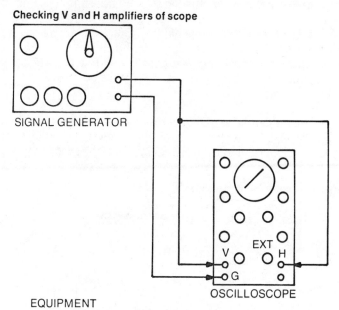

SIGNAL GENERATOR

OSCILLOSCOPE

EQUIPMENT

SIGNAL GENERATOR
OSCILLOSCOPE BEING TESTED

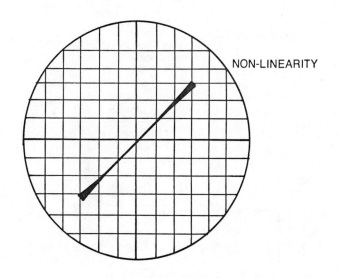

NON-LINEARITY

## CHECKING A SCOPE FOR PHASE SHIFT

Since an oscilloscope is a measuring instrument, it is important for the operator to know if it is measuring or interpreting correctly what is fed to it. Phase shift occuring in an audio amplifier will appear as an Lissajous ellipse on a scope CRT rather than a diagonal line. But, if the scope suffers from the same sickness, an ellipse will also be observed and wasted hours will probably be spent trying to cure a healthy amplifier instead of having the scope circuits put in order.

### Procedure

Connect an audio signal generator to the scope as shown in the illustration. The hot lead of the generator connects to both the horizontal and the vertical inputs of the scope with the

**Checking scope for phase shift**

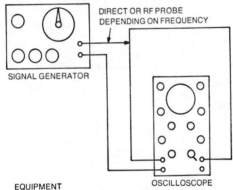

DIRECT OR RF PROBE
DEPENDING ON FREQUENCY

SIGNAL GENERATOR

EQUIPMENT

OSCILLOSCOPE

SIGNAL GENERATOR
OSCILLOSCOPE CONNECTED TOGETHER BY MEANS OF A
DIRECT PROBE IN AUDIO FREQUENCIES, BUT WITH AN RF
PROBE IN THE RADIO FREQUENCY RANGES.

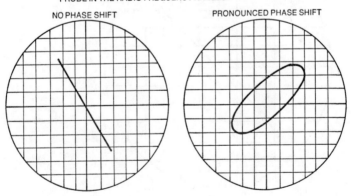

NO PHASE SHIFT

PRONOUNCED PHASE SHIFT

ground connection to the scope's ground. The horizontal control is set to external. Begin with some low frequency, say 400 Hz, and observe the trace. A straight diagonal line is what you should get if all is right. Gradually turn up the frequency range on the scope, matching the upward ranging generator. Do this until the upper limits of the scope or generator, is reached whichever has the lower capability. If an ellipse appears at some high frequency, that means that phase shift exists at that point, and the scope is unreliable for phase shift measurement beyond that point. If phase shift exists in the scope at low frequencies, the scope should go to the repair shop.

While a certain amount of phase shift is allowable when one reaches the upper frequency limits of the scope, it is not tolerable in the lower frequencies where all of the audio checking is done.

## CHECKING CAPACITANCE OF A SCOPE'S ATTENUATORS

Every step of the coarse attenuator control of an oscilloscope should have the same input capacitance, or else the resulting readings will vary as the input is switched from one step to the other. A scope long in service may have one or more steps not in the same ratio to each other, due to components aging in those circuits. To make certain that each step is capacitatively accurate, the simple test shown here will remove any doubts you may have.

### Procedure

Connect a signal generator to the scope as shown in the illustration. Tune the generator so that it is producing a sine or square (or even triangle) wave at some frequency between 50 kHz and 100 kHz. The waveform is unimportant, since the scope's horizontal gain is set low to obtain a straight vertical line trace. Switch S1 is flipped to Position 1, which shorts out the trimmer capacitor. Use the vertical gain control so that the vertical line is of some convenient height which is easy to read. The actual length is unimportant as long as that control is not disturbed during the test. Now phase switch S1 to Position 2. The trimmer capacitor is now in the circuit. Adjust it so the trace is reduced by exactly half of the previous reading. For the rest of the test do not touch it again. Move the scope coarse attenuator switch to the next position, repeating the previous test. If all is well, in each case the vertical trace will be reduced by one-half.

**Checking capacitance of scope's attenuators**

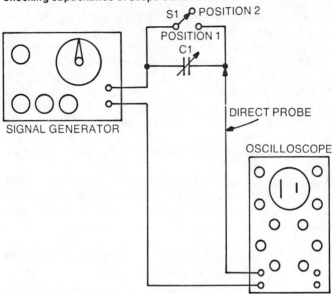

EQUIPMENT

SIGNAL GENERATOR SET AT SOME FREQUENCY BETWEEN 100 and 1 kHz
S1—SINGLE-POLE, SINGLE-THROW SWITCH
C1—VARIABLE CAPACITOR, VALUE IS UNIMPORTANT
SCOPE BEING TESTED

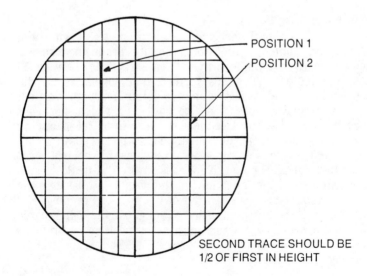

## ADJUSTMENT OF ATTENUATOR
## PROBE TO ELIMINATE DISTORTION

An attenuator probe allows the viewing of signals that would be otherwise impossible to see on a scope. A direct probe causes no loss of signal, as does the attenuator probe, but certain circuits are detuned by using the direct probe. This is due to loading by the cable and the scope input. The attenuator reduces the signal by usually 1/10, but since it offers a chance to observe signals of delicate circuits, the probe is often used in spite of this one disadvantage. The attenuator probe must be adjusted to avoid the introduction of distortion, which could be mistaken as originating within the circuit being checked. A square wave generator offers a fast and simple means of seeing if the attenuator circuit is cutting the signal down by exactly 1/10 and if any distortion is being introduced by the probe.

### Procedure

Most attenuator probes contain some variation of the circuit shown in the illustration. R1 will range from 2 to 5 megohms, while R2 will be from 200 K to 1 meg. The tunable capacitor, C1, will range from 5 to 20 pF and is adjustable by means of the screw on the casing. This adjustment should provide a means of obtaining a distortionless square wave.

The signal generator's output is fed to the tip of the probe and its ground clip. This in turn is connected to the vertical

**Adjustment of attenuator probe**

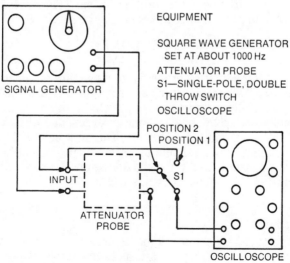

EQUIPMENT

SQUARE WAVE GENERATOR
  SET AT ABOUT 1000 Hz
ATTENUATOR PROBE
S1—SINGLE-POLE, DOUBLE
  THROW SWITCH
OSCILLOSCOPE

SIGNAL GENERATOR

POSITION 2
  POSITION 1

INPUT

S1

ATTENUATOR
PROBE

OSCILLOSCOPE

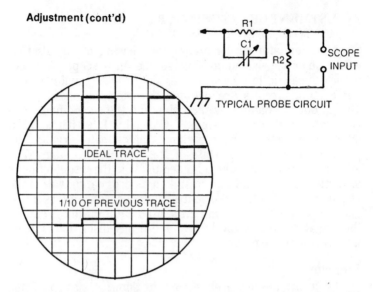

inputs of the scope. Make certain that the signal trace is high enough to be easily measured. Now pass the signal directly to the probe, bypassing the attenuator circuit by placing switch S1 in position 1. Now move the switch to its other position and observe the trace height. It should be 1/10 of the original trace. To make certain, move the vertical attenuator switch on the scope down one step. This should multiply the trace by ten, which means that now the trace will be as high as it was before the probe was put into the circuit. Observe the square wave as you slowly turn the screw on the casing. The corners of the trace should be as square as the original trace.

## DETERMINING THE UPPER LIMITS OF A DEMODULATOR PROBE

The demodulator probe is a necessary adjunct to an oscilloscope when checking a circuit in which a modulator exists. A radio receiver is one such example. However, a demodulator probe has its limits—frequency-wise. Beyond that limit it introduces distortion. The limit beyond which the probe cannot be used should be known to the user, as he would otherwise assume that the distortion he observes in a circuit at certain high frequencies is due to the circuit and not to the probe.

### Procedure

The output of the RF signal generator is connected to the input of the modulator circuit, as is the output of the square

**Determining upper limits of demodulator probe**

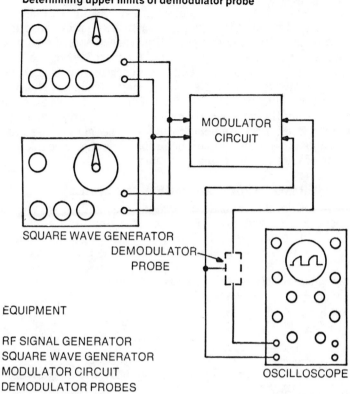

MODULATOR
CIRCUIT

SQUARE WAVE GENERATOR

DEMODULATOR
PROBE

EQUIPMENT

RF SIGNAL GENERATOR
SQUARE WAVE GENERATOR
MODULATOR CIRCUIT
DEMODULATOR PROBES
OSCILLOSCOPE

OSCILLOSCOPE

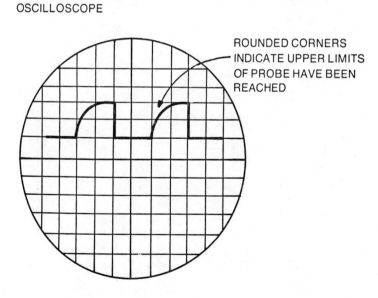

ROUNDED CORNERS
INDICATE UPPER LIMITS
OF PROBE HAVE BEEN
REACHED

119

wave generator. The modulator's output then goes to the oscilloscope via a demodulator probe. Begin with a low frequency and an output voltage which will not overload the input of the circuit under test. The frequency of the square wave generator is slowly raised until the waveform on the CRT shows signs of rounding off at the upper corner. The scope picture drawing depicts distortion being introduced, showing the upper limits of the probe have been passed. Decrease the frequency of the square wave generator until the distortion has disappeared. The frequency read on the generator's dial indicates the upper limits of the probe. This should be marked on the probe as a reminding safeguard.

## MEASURING CAPACITANCE OF A DC PROBE

A DC probe is used in conjunction with a VTVM to measure DC voltages. The circuit within the probe is essentially a low-pass filter. This filter circuit greatly reduces the capacitance inherent in the cable of the probe. Precisely

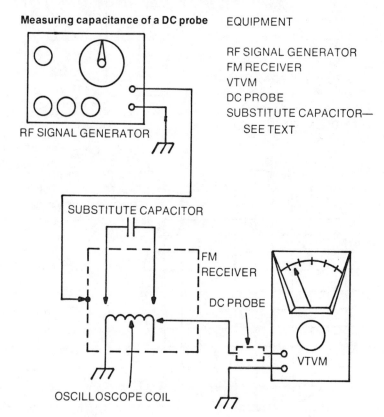

**Measuring capacitance of a DC probe**

EQUIPMENT

RF SIGNAL GENERATOR
FM RECEIVER
VTVM
DC PROBE
SUBSTITUTE CAPACITOR—
    SEE TEXT

RF SIGNAL GENERATOR

SUBSTITUTE CAPACITOR

FM RECEIVER

DC PROBE

VTVM

OSCILLOSCOPE COIL

because of this reduced capacitance, which can cause erroneous measurements, the exact capacitance of the probe must be known. The test is done with the arrangement shown in the figure.

### Procedure

The RF signal generator is connected to an FM receiver. The latter is tuned to some station. The generator's frequency is tuned until the tone zero beats against the station signal. When this occurs the two signals blend and no beat signal can be heard. The DC probe of the VTVM is applied to the oscillator coil of the receiver. The generator is now retuned for a zero beat. Remove the DC probe and substitute capacitors across the coil as shown in the illustration. Once a capacitor is found which causes zero beating, its value will be equal to the input capacitance of the DC probe.

## CHECKING THE FREQUENCY RANGE OF A VTVM

Whereas a VOM will measure an AC voltage most accurately at line frequency, or 60 Hz, a VTVM will go much higher. The question is, how much higher? What are the upper limits to which the meter of the VTVM will respond? It is wise to know just what these upper limits are while the manufacturer specifies this in the owner's manual, this does not mean that years later, the VTVM is still accurate at its upper limit.

### Procedure

It is best to have a sweep generator instead of an ordinary signal generator for this test. This does not mean that the test cannot be carried out if one does not own a sweep generator; it merely means that a graph must be plotted out as shown in the illustration. The graph is marked VOLTAGE on the vertical axis and FREQUENCY on the horizontal. Connect the output of the generator directly to the input of the VTVM. The latter should be set to read some voltage which must remain constant during the test. Sweep the frequency—manually or with a sweep generator—over several frequencies. Make certain that the output voltage of the generator remains constant during the entire test. The output voltage must not vary at all for accurate results. Begin at some low frequency and mark the output voltage for that frequency on the graph. Continue upwards until the VTVM shows a decided drop in its AC voltage reading. That is its upper limit. Beyond that, the readings will be a hit-and-miss affair.

**Checking the frequency range of a VTVM**

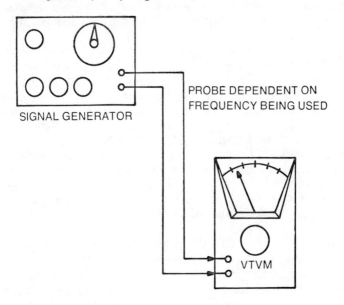

PROBE DEPENDENT ON
FREQUENCY BEING USED

SIGNAL GENERATOR

VTVM

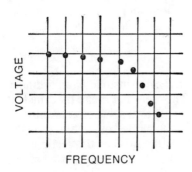

VOLTAGE

FREQUENCY

EQUIPMENT

SIGNAL GENERATOR OR SWEEP GENERATOR
PROBES—TYPE WILL DEPEND ON THE FREQUENCIES BEING
USED
VTVM BEING CHECKED

122

# Chapter 5

# Using The

# Signal Generator

If you have purchased a signal generator, or built one from a kit, your owner's operating manual provides basic instructions on how to use your test instrument. However, a manual of that type cannot contain all of the knowledge and skills gained by years of experience of actually using the instrument. Gathered here, in this chapter, are various ways in which to use a signal generator to perform alignments, measurements and checks.

## ALIGNING AN AM BROADCAST RECEIVER

A misaligned AM set shows up with oscillations between stations, hissing, or no signal on the stations. In some versions of a misaligned set, only the stations in the middle of the band can be tuned in. Aligning a set is not difficult, but care is needed for good results. When a station is tuned properly, the voltage reading will rise sharply at that point. This is the principle of the test explained below.

### Procedure

First, disable the AVC and AGC circuits. The receiver is tuned to an open spot near the top (high end) of the dial. There should be no sound of a station at that frequency. The local oscillator tuning capacitor is then shorted out. The RF signal generator is tuned to the I-F frequency of the receiver, which is usually 455 kHz. Use a low output setting for the generator, but the volume of the receiver turned up to maximum. A low voltage should now be read on the VTVM. Use an alignment tool to turn the slug inside the coil of the primary and the secondary of the last I-F transformer to obtain a maximum reading on the meter. A sharp peak should be seen when the coil slug is twisted. Adjust the slugs in the coils for the other stages, working backwards through the stages toward the antenna. Keep the generator's output level low for maximum sensitivity. Be careful of overloading.

The short from the local oscillator tuning capacitor should now be removed. Couple the generator's output cable to the antenna or lay the cable so it is close to it. The signal generator and the receiver are now tuned to 1400 kHz. Adjust the oscillator trimmer for maximum reading. Do the same for the RF amplifier trimmer and the antenna trimmer capacitors.

Now tune the receiver and the generator to 600 kHz and adjust the oscillator tuning slug for maximum output. Since adjusting one coil may affect another stage, it is a good idea to repeat the steps several times until no further improvement can be seen.

**Aligning an AM broadcast receiver**

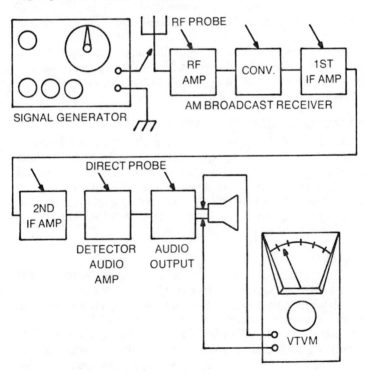

## MEASURING SENSITIVITY OF AN FM RECEIVER

Receiver sensitivity is always listed in the owner's manual. But, as the FM receiver ages, things happen to it which includes changes in its sensitivity. It is a good idea to check this periodically to know just what the sensitivity is at that moment. The test is simple and requires a minimum of equipment to determine the minimum signal strength to which the receiver responds.

### Procedure

First, the squelch circuit must be disabled. Second, a reading of the noise voltage must be taken. (How to measure noise voltage is described elsewhere in this book.) Third, apply a continuous wave (CW) signal at the frequency to which the receiver is tuned by using an RF signal generator, through its RF probe, connected to the input of the FM receiver. The receiver output is terminated with a load resistor with the probes of the VTVM connected across it. The output of the generator is gradually increased from a low figure until the

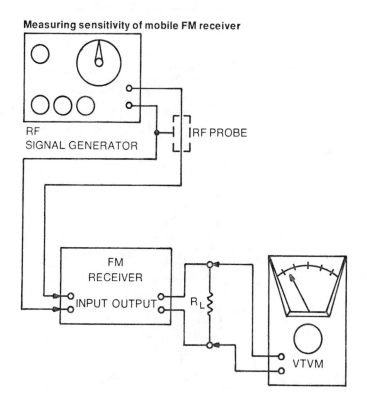

Measuring sensitivity of mobile FM receiver

125

noise ratio drops 20 dB. If the VTVM is not marked in dB, consider this figure to be equivalent to a 10% drop in noise. Then, all that remains is to measure the voltage (in microvolts) which saturated the limiter to such a point that the noise voltage dropped 20 dB or 10%.

## ADJUSTING SEPARATION IN FM MPX RECEIVER

This test can only be performed with a square wave generator used in conjunction with an FM MPX (stereo) generator. The stereo generator provides the needed

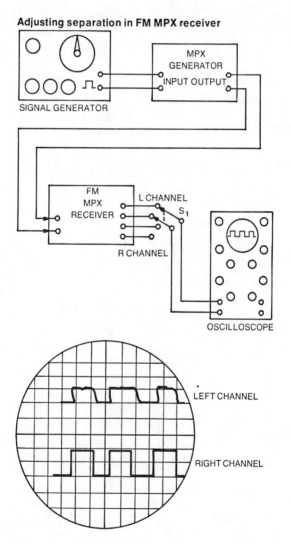

**Adjusting separation in FM MPX receiver**

information as to distortion and, above all, the separation of the two signals which make up the right and left channels.

## Procedure

The square wave generator is tuned to some frequency between 1 kHz and 5 kHz. Within this range, no integration of the square wave will result. The output voltage of the generator should be set low enough so that there is no overload. The input of the stereo generator is connected to the output of the square wave generator and the output of the MPX generator to the point in the receiver where a composite audio signal is found. Both outputs of the receiver are fed to the vertical amplifiers of the scope.

With a dual-trace scope, both traces are visible simultaneously. With a switch, each channel can be observed successively on a single-trace scope. One channel may produce a square wave and the other may show a smaller and more distorted waveform. The separation control is then turned slowly to obtain a point at which the best traces are seen.

## FM STEREO ALIGNMENT AID

When aligning a stereo multiplex receiver, an accurate 19 kHz signal source is required to properly tune the internal multiplex oscillator. In the absence of a crystal-controlled signal generator source, an audio generator can be used. Here's how:

Connect an antenna to the FM receiver and tune in a station known to be transmitting in stereo. Adjust the audio signal generator to approximately 19 kHz. Using a 10,000 ohm resistor in series with the hot output lead of the generator, inject the signal into the receiver circuit between the FM detector and the multiplex input. Adjust the audio generator slowly until a zero beat is heard in the receiver's speaker. The audio generator is now tuned to 19 kHz.

## SIGNAL GENERATOR AS GRID DIP OSCILLATOR

A grid dip oscillator is a handy tool to have, but unless you have frequent need for the instrument, it does not pay to own one. A signal generator in conjunction with a VOM makes a simple and inexpensive substitute. The meter in the VOM should be no less sensitive than 500 $\mu$A full scale. Plug-in coils allow the oscillator in the circuit shown in the illustration to be tuned over many ranges. The principle is that when the coil is adjusted to resonate with the tuned circuit, there is a sudden dip in the grid current. This is caused by the absorption of the energy by the tuned circuit. This gives you a null point. The rf signal generator in our version provides the variable capacitor and the VOM indicates the null.

## Procedure

Connect the RF generator to the adapter circuit by means of coaxial cable, since you are dealing with radio frequencies. For the same reason, all leads should be kept as short as possible. The coil, L1, is chosen to have a range which will cause it to oscillate with the circuit in question. The diode rectifies the current so that it can be read by the VOM set on DC ranges. Adjust the meter so that a drop in current will cause a sharp deflection of the meter needle.

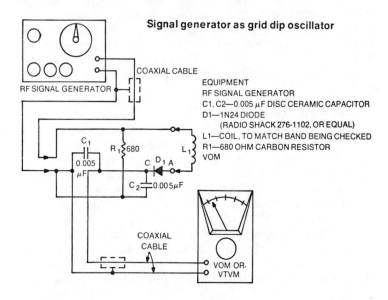

**Signal generator as grid dip oscillator**

EQUIPMENT
RF SIGNAL GENERATOR
C1, C2—0.005 µF DISC CERAMIC CAPACITOR
D1—1N24 DIODE
(RADIO SHACK 276-1102, OR EQUAL)
L1—COIL, TO MATCH BAND BEING CHECKED
R1—680 OHM CARBON RESISTOR
VOM

## MEASURING INPUT IMPEDANCE OF LOW IMPEDANCE CIRCUIT

Knowing the input impedance of a circuit is a useful parameter to be aware of. A signal generator and one potentiometer, plus a fixed resistor and an AC VTVM, are all the instruments one needs to have to carry out this measurement.

## Procedure

The output of the signal generator is connected to the input of the circuit under test through the two resistors and the switch. The output of the circuit is connected to the input of the

AC VTVM. The generator should be set at a very low frequency—about 20 Hz. This frequency avoids input of capacitance of the circuit under test entering into the calculations which have to be carried out. R1, the fixed resistor, should be at least ten times the possible impedance of the circuit under test. The potentiometer, R2, will range from 1 K to 1 meg. First, the voltmeter is used to measure the output of the circuit without R2. This is done by placing S1 in position 1. Now flip the switch so that the pot is back into the circuit. Adjust the pot until you get a reading in volts which is half to the pervious reading. Next, the pot is taken out of the circuit and the active resistance is measured carefully so as not to disturb the pot's resistance setting. That resistance is equal to the input impedance of the circuit being measured.

**Measuring input impedance of low impedance circuit**

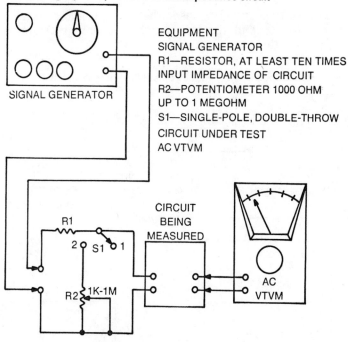

EQUIPMENT
SIGNAL GENERATOR
R1—RESISTOR, AT LEAST TEN TIMES
INPUT IMPEDANCE OF CIRCUIT
R2—POTENTIOMETER 1000 OHM
UP TO 1 MEGOHM
S1—SINGLE-POLE, DOUBLE-THROW
CIRCUIT UNDER TEST
AC VTVM

## MEASURING INPUT IMPEDANCE
## OF HIGH IMPEDANCE CIRCUIT

Although at first glance, this method is similar to the previous test (measuring low impedance circuit) there is a slight difference in the arrangement of the potentiometer. The theory behind the two of them is similar, as can be seen when carrying out the experiments.

**Procedure**

Many of the modern circuits, due to the use of FETs or ICs, have very high input impedances, which cannot be measured by the system last described. This system works best for circuits having an input impedance ranging from 1 K to 220 K. Again, the generator is set at a very low frequency—about 20 Hz. Voltage level is unimportant, just so the reading can be obtained on the VTVM. The level is read with S1 bypassing the potentiometer, R1. The later can be any unit from 100K all the way up to 5 megohms. Several may have to be tried until a reading is gotten on the meter. Change the position of the switch to position 1 so that the reading now includes R1. Adjust R1 so that a reading is obtained, which is exactly half of the first reading, when S1 was in position 2. That part of the pot which was in the circuit is now measured (out of circuit) and this resistance is equal to the input impedance of the circuit being tested.

**Measuring input impedance of high impedance circuit**

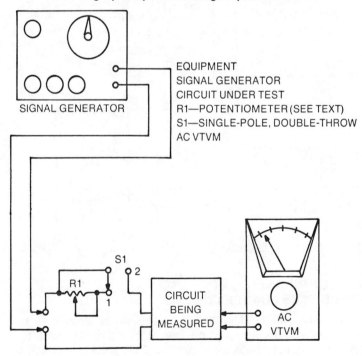

SIGNAL GENERATOR

EQUIPMENT
SIGNAL GENERATOR
CIRCUIT UNDER TEST
R1—POTENTIOMETER (SEE TEXT)
S1—SINGLE-POLE, DOUBLE-THROW
AC VTVM

S1

R1

CIRCUIT
BEING
MEASURED

AC
VTVM

## DETERMINING RESONANT
## FREQUENCY OF TUNED CIRCUIT

It is often necessary to determine the resonant point of a circuit, either one standing by itself, or one that is part of a larger component. A signal generator offers a simple, but very accurate, means of finding at what point the tuned circuit will resonate.

### Procedure

The RF signal generator output is fed to the input of the circuit under test. The ground lead is connected to the ground of the VTVM. RF probes are used throughout. The probes of the VTVM are connected across the load resistor, which connects the circuit to ground. This resistor, R1, should have a value of about 1500 ohms. The generator's output should be unmodulated for this test. Begin with a frequency lower than the estimated resonant point of the circuit under test. Gradually raise the output frequency until the needle on the meter of the VTVM shows a sudden drop. This is the resonant point. It is a good idea to continue sweeping to make certain that this is the fundamental and not a harmonic. Any harmonic will deflect the needle much less than the fundamental which draws more power. Once you are satisfied the resonant point has been reached, it is a simple matter to read the frequency from the dial of the generator, or whatever means are used on your generator to determine exact frequencies.

**Determining resonant point of tuned circuit**

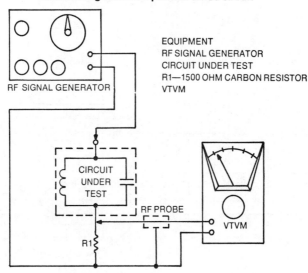

EQUIPMENT
RF SIGNAL GENERATOR
CIRCUIT UNDER TEST
R1—1500 OHM CARBON RESISTOR
VTVM

RF SIGNAL GENERATOR

CIRCUIT UNDER TEST

RF PROBE

VTVM

R1

## MEASURING UNKNOWN FREQUENCIES

Using an accurately calibrated AF generator in conjunction with an oscilloscope enables unknown frequencies to be measured quite accurately. The principle is that if the known frequency of the generator matches that of the unknown frequency, a circle is seen on the CRT.

However, should the unknown be beyond the range of the generator, it can still be measured with the same method. In this case, Lissajous figures are employed. The number of circles tangential to the H axis (known frequency) are compared to the number tangential to the V axis (unknown frequency). The ratio between the circles is then the ratio between the two frequencies.

**Measuring unknown frequency**

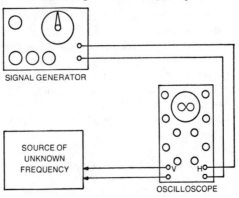

IN THIS EXAMPLE
UNKNOWN = 2/1 × KNOWN FREQUENCY

IN THIS EXAMPLE
UNKNOWN ≈ 1/3 × KNOWN

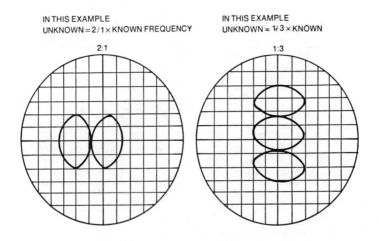

2:1

1:3

## Procedure

The scope's external selector is set to EXT. The signal generator is connected to the H-inputs and the unknown to the V inputs. The generator's frequency is increased until a circle appears. The unknown frequency is then equal to the setting of the generator. The Lissajous figures indicate multiples or submultiples of the known frequency.

The equation is,

$$\text{Unknown Frequency} = \frac{V \text{ points}}{H \text{ points}} \times \text{Frequency}$$

## MEASURING AC RESISTANCE OF A RESONANT CIRCUIT

An audio generator, with the addition of two 1% resistors and a potentiometer, provide an accurate way of measuring a series or parallel resonant circuit. The same technique is used for either circuit. As in any bridge configuration, the potentiometer is adjusted to produce a null reading in the meter.

## Procedure

The equation used is:

$$Rx = \frac{R1 \times R3}{R2}$$

where Rx is the unknown circuit being measured
R1 and R2 are 1% resistors
R3 is a potentiometer, preferably calibrated

**Measuring AC resistance of resonant circuit**

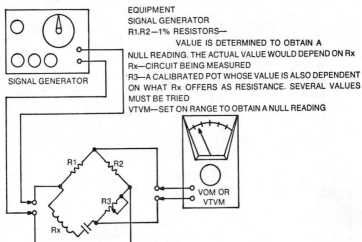

EQUIPMENT
SIGNAL GENERATOR
R1,R2—1% RESISTORS—
         VALUE IS DETERMINED TO OBTAIN A
NULL READING. THE ACTUAL VALUE WOULD DEPEND ON Rx
Rx—CIRCUIT BEING MEASURED
R3—A CALIBRATED POT WHOSE VALUE IS ALSO DEPENDENT
ON WHAT Rx OFFERS AS RESISTANCE. SEVERAL VALUES
MUST BE TRIED
VTVM—SET ON RANGE TO OBTAIN A NULL READING

SIGNAL GENERATOR

VOM OR
VTVM

R1    R2
R3
Rx

The equipment for the test is set up as shown. The actual values for R1 and R2 are relatively unimportant. If equal, they cancel each other out and the resistance of the circuit is basically that of the resistance of the pot. A calibrated pot is a big help, however without one it is still possible to conduct the test. Slowly rotate the control until a sharp null is reached. Take the pot out of the bridge, and without touching the control, measure that part of its resistance which was placed in the circuit. That value is placed in the equation above. The resistance measured is the AC resistance at the resonant point of the circuit. The generator's frequency can be anywhere from 1 kHz to 3 kHz.

## DUMMY LOAD FOR GENERATOR

When troubleshooting an AM receiver, usually every stage needs to be checked—and the obvious place to begin is at the antenna. But, connecting the signal generator directly to the antenna may cause spurious signals to appear. To avoid creating problems, use the circuit described as a dummy antenna load. This prevents loading an AM receiver.

**Dummy antenna load**

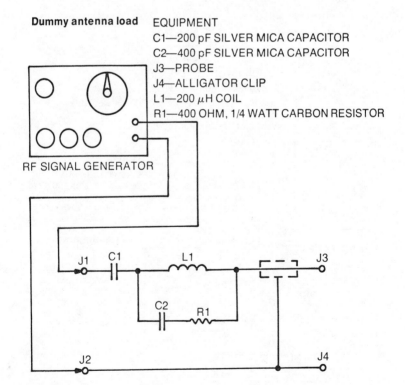

EQUIPMENT
C1—200 pF SILVER MICA CAPACITOR
C2—400 pF SILVER MICA CAPACITOR
J3—PROBE
J4—ALLIGATOR CLIP
L1—200 $\mu$H COIL
R1—400 OHM, 1/4 WATT CARBON RESISTOR

134

## Procedure

The four components shown in the illustration are assembled in a metal can. It is even better to place them inside an empty probe casing, provided miniature components are chosen. Probe casings are available in most electronic stores and are seen commonly in their mail-order catalogs. A coaxial cable is employed to connect the dummy load to the receiver. Any type of terminals may be used depending on your own preferences. The ground side is best ended with an alligator clip. J1 and J2 are left up to your judgement. The advantage of the circuit is that the receiver will "see" an impedance which matches that of an AM receiver antenna. This circuit allows the RF generator to be put to use with any AM set from 550 kHz to 30 MHz.

## CHECKING AMPLITUDE DISTORTION

Non-linearity of a video amplifier, also known as amplitude distortion, is a symptom of several electronic

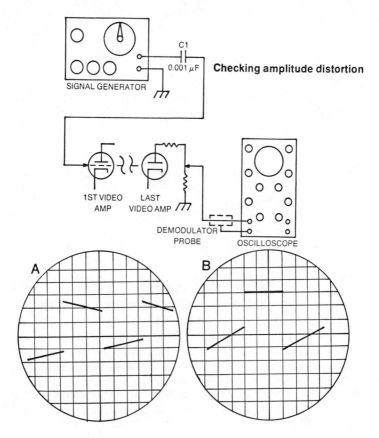

Checking amplitude distortion

diseases which affect TV circuits. For that matter, any amplifier may display this symptom. If amplitude distortion exists, the result of the square wave produced by the signal generator will show an asymmetrical tilt. The wave is run through the total amplifier stages and the result is checked on the scope.

## Procedure

Connect the output of a square-wave generator to the input of the first video amplifier; the input of the scope is connected to the last video amp. Note that a demodulator probe must be used to connect the scope to the amplifier. Set the generator at a frequency below 60 Hz. A small capacitance (0.001 $\mu$F) is connected in series with the high-impedance probe of the generator. There is bound to be some tilt but it should be symmetrical, as in illustration A. Scope picture B, on the other hand, shows enough non-linearity to make the results objectionable.

## PLOTTING A BAND-PASS CURVE

A signal generator permits plotting a band-pass curve, as in the TV set shown in the illustration. A sweep generator gives an almost instant picture of the total curve; without it, one can use an RF signal generator. The only difference is that point after point must be plotted on graph paper to obtain the curve. It just takes longer, that is all.

## Procedure

The instruments are connected as shown. Do not forget that RF probes must be used during the course of this test. First, disconnect the antenna with the terminals in back of the set shorted together. The VTVM is connected across the load resistor of the picture detector. It is set to read low DC voltages. The generator, through its probes, is connected to the mixer section of the tuner. To couple the signal generator capacitively to the set, lift up the shield of the mixer tube so that it is not grounded. Then clip the generator's lead to the shield. A graph should be prepared as in the illustration. The vertical or Y axis is marked in volts—0.5 volt increments are about right. The horizontal, or X axis, represents the frequency in MHz. The axis scale is marked off in 0.25 or 0.5 MHz increments. Set the generator's frequency at some low point and adjust for the lowest output voltage. The setting of the generator should not be touched during the course of the test. At each increment in frequency change, read the voltage on the VTVM and mark that point on the graph paper. Cover the entire spectrum of the frequency and mark as many points as you feel will give you a thoroughly rounded picture of the band-pass curve.

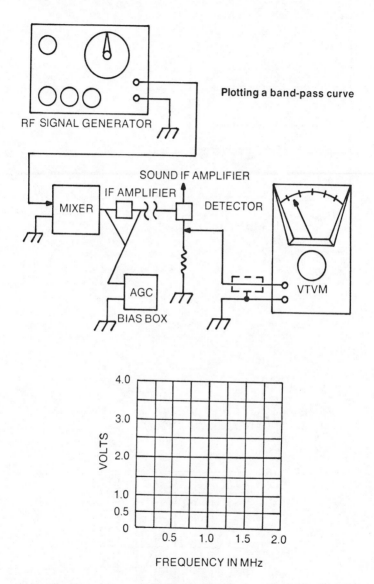

Plotting a band-pass curve

## PLOTTING THE FREQUENCY CURVE OF AN EQUALIZER

The equalizer, regardless of its characteristics, has a cut-off point, but these characteristics cannot be expressed by

137

**Plotting frequency curve of equalizer**

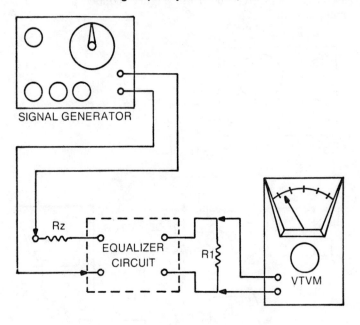

EQUIPMENT

SIGNAL GENERATOR
Rz—600 OHMS
R1—EQUAL TO OUTPUT IMPEDANCE OF THE CIRCUIT
VTVM, SET TO READ LOW AC VOLTAGES

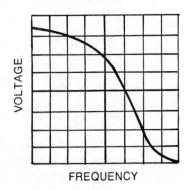

a straight line. A curve, such as the one shown in the illustration, is an example of such an equalizer. Graph paper is made for this express purpose. The vertical axis should be marked in voltages and the horizontal axis in frequency.

## Procedure

The output generator is set at a frequency below which the equalizer does not take effect. A sine wave is the best for our use in this test. The output of the generator goes to the equalizer circuit through the resistor, Rz. This resistor would be 600 ohms in the case of the standard 600 ohm line being used. Now raise the frequency while the reading of the VTVM is noted. The VTVM is connected across R1, which should match the output impedance of the circuit being tested. Take voltage readings as the frequency is raised. The closer they are to each other the smoother the resulting curve will be. The curve will then represent the frequency response of the equalizer.

## CHECKING RF AMPLIFIER GAIN

With the aid of a signal generator, any AM, FM or TV amplifier can be checked to obtain an over-all idea of its performance. The same method may be used, for that matter, for any RF amplifier.

## Procedure

The signal generator should be tuned to a frequency within the range of the AM or FM receiver; in the case of a TV set being checked, the channel picture-carrier frequency is used instead. If you have only a low frequency generator, a harmonic of the fundamental frequency can be used. This means using a square wave to employ its harmonics.

The VTVM is set to read DC and is connected across the output load resistor of the second detector stage. The AGC is disabled and an external bias supply is connected. The RF amplifier is set at maximum gain with the generator's attenuator control also set to maximum. While observing the VTVM, lower the generator's output to the point where the reading on the VTVM's meter just begins to show a deflection. The generator's output is connected to the antenna, using S1 in position 1. Take the reading. Now switch S1 to position 2, so that the generator is connected to the mixer stage. The reading should be much lower. Each channel of a TV set should be tested the same way to obtain an overall picture of the performance of the amplifier.

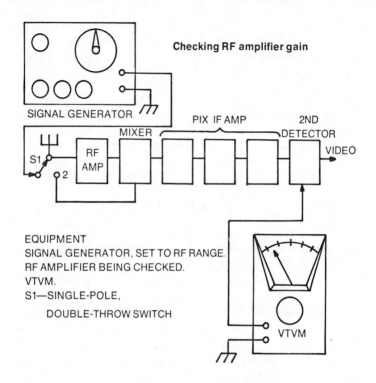

Checking RF amplifier gain

EQUIPMENT
SIGNAL GENERATOR, SET TO RF RANGE.
RF AMPLIFIER BEING CHECKED.
VTVM.
S1—SINGLE-POLE,
    DOUBLE-THROW SWITCH

## MEASURING GAIN IN A VIDEO AMPLIFIER

While a video amplifier may be operating to some degree, unless the gain is measured we have no way of knowing precisely how well it is working. The test illustrated below allows us to form a ratio between the input and the output voltages in order to obtain the actual amount of gain to be expected from the amplifier. A drastically reduced gain indicates problems arising from defective tubes, something wrong with the power supply, or components whose values have changed.

### Procedure

The AM signal generator is connected to the sound takeoff coil. This is done with a demodulator probe, since we are going to inject a signal with a frequency of 4.5 MHz. Some 30% modulation should be allowed for this test. First, the demodulator probe of the oscilloscope is applied to point A. This will give us a measurement of the input voltage. Now bring the probe to point B. This gives us the voltage as amplified by the 4.5 MHz I-F amplifier. The scope should have been calibrated previously to obtain true arithmetical ratios from this test. The generator, TV set, and the scope should be warmed up at least five minutes before testing, to avoid inaccuracies.

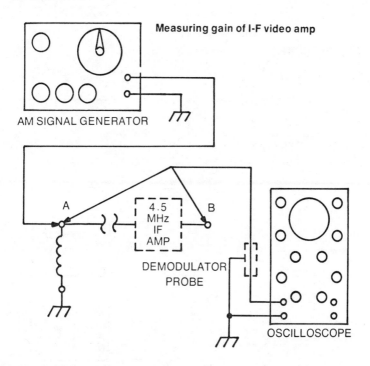

Measuring gain of I-F video amp

## CHECKING I-F STAGES IN A TV SET

The technique used to check the amplifier stages in a TV set is similar to that used in signal tracing with any type of amplifier. There are, however, two differences: the I-F frequency must be modulated and a demodulator probe must be used. This is a signal tracing technique, as no gain nor voltage measurements can be obtained, due to the loading characteristics of the probe. All that you are able to do is to establish that a signal is going through each stage with a slight indication of significant gain.

### Procedure

The RF signal generator is connected to a modulator circuit. A typical modulator circuit is shown in the illustration. If the generator has a built-in modulator, then the outboard circuit is unnecessary. The modulator output is applied through the probe grid of each tube of the I-F stages. The switch, S1, is a quick way of shifting the demodulator probe from the grid to the plate to the vertical inputs of the scope. A dead stage shows up by the lack of a video pattern on the scope.

**Checking I-F stages in TV**

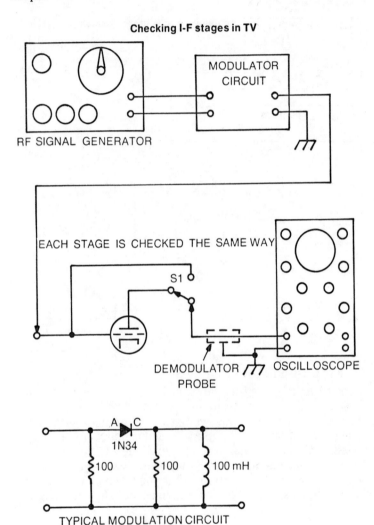

RF SIGNAL GENERATOR

MODULATOR CIRCUIT

EACH STAGE IS CHECKED THE SAME WAY

S1

DEMODULATOR PROBE

OSCILLOSCOPE

A C
1N34

100   100   100 mH

TYPICAL MODULATION CIRCUIT

## CHECKING LINEARITY OF A TV SET

The linearity of a TV set is easy to check. Furthermore, this test has the advantage that the back of the set does not have to be opened. When one is not certain as to what they are doing, the results of a carelessly applied finger to high voltage can be painful—when it is not lethal. But, for this test, only two controls need to be adjusted and both are located on the side or the back of the set.

**Procedure**

A modulated RF signal from the signal generator is applied to the antenna terminals of the TV set. The signal should be at about 55 MHz and should be connected by means of an RF probe. Tune to channel two. The results should consist of equally spaced black and white lines on the screen of the set. Make certain the set is warmed up properly—allow at least five minutes before any adjustments are made. If the lines are not of equal spacing, then the sets vertical linearity is at fault. Locate the controls and adjust the bottom of the picture by means of the height control while the vertical linearity control is adjusted for the top of the picture. Both controls may need to be manipulated to obtain a completely linear picture.

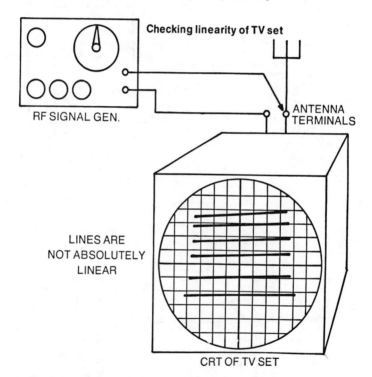

Checking linearity of TV set

RF SIGNAL GEN.

ANTENNA TERMINALS

LINES ARE NOT ABSOLUTELY LINEAR

CRT OF TV SET

## SWEEP ALIGNMENT OF AN I-F AMPLIFIER

Aligning an I-F amplifier stage is not too complicated. But, due to the many frequencies involved in that stage within a TV set, alignment requires the use of a sweep generator. The illustration shows the connections necessary to obtain a significant sweep. However, the instructions for your own model of sweep generator should be checked for the actual connections.

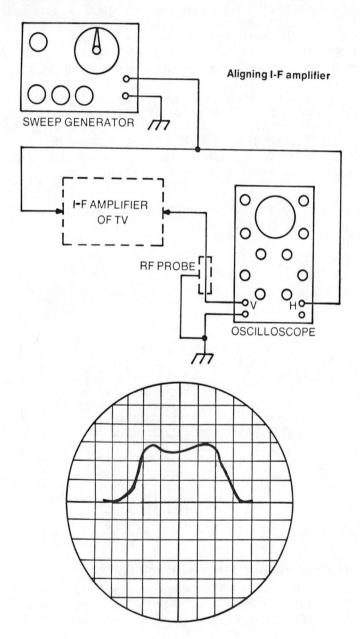

Aligning I-F amplifier

SWEEP GENERATOR

I-F AMPLIFIER OF TV

RF PROBE

OSCILLOSCOPE

## Procedure

The sweep generator is set at a frequency sweep which will encompass the range of the I-F amplifier stage. The vertical input of the scope is attached via an RF probe to the I-F output of the TV set. The scope horizontal input is connected to the horizontal signal output of the sweep generator. Alignment should be done carefully using a plastic alignment tool inside the slug of the I-F coil. At some point, when the alignment is done correctly, a waveform somewhat similar to a square wave will appear. There will be however a dip occurring between the top corners of the wave. These are at 41 and 48 MHz. Be very careful when turning the slug, as it is very easy to jam it into the coil in such a way that the coil must be replaced.

# Chapter 6

# Checking Components

The signal generator, being a versatile instrument, can be used in conjunction with other units such as an oscilloscope or a VTVM (plus some simple formulas here and there) to measure various parameters of individual electronic components. Tests such as these are invaluable when troubleshooting existing circuit components or designing new circuits. This chapter explains how to test resistors, capacitors, inductances, diodes and transistors.

## MATCHING AND COMPARING RESISTORS

Incorrectly marked resistors occur and, even if this is infrequent, it can lead to hours of futile troubleshooting in a circuit in which such a resistor has been employed. Then too, we must not forget resistors whose values have changed, or where the markings are erased. Also, there are circuits in which precise matching of resistors is absolutely necessary. The scope in the arrangement below compares the voltage appearing at Point "A" with that appearing at Point "B." If the resistors are equal, the voltage will be the same at both points and so will be the height of the trace on the CRT.

### Procedure

The frequency used is not important. In fact, the scope horizontal gain can be turned down so that only a straight line results. Clip the positive probe to the standard resistor. The ground probe is applied to the signal generator ground. Adjust

**Matching or comparing resistors**

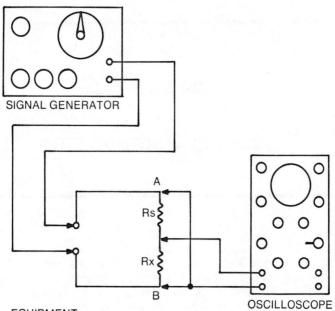

EQUIPMENT
SIGNAL GENERATOR
Rs—STANDARD RESISTOR
OSCILLOSCOPE, SET TO READ THE SIGNAL GENERATOR
FREQUENCY.

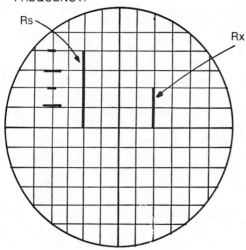

the trace by means of the signal generator output or by the scope vertical gain so that the trace occupies so many divisions. The voltage from the generator can be from 2 to 10 volts. Now, move the signal probe to point B. If the resistors are equal, the height of the trace will be equal. Note that the height of the trace for Rs (the standard resistor) is twice that of Rx, the unknown resistor. If Rs is 50 ohms, we know that Rx must be 25 ohms, the height of the trace being proportional to the voltage dropped—due to the resistance in the circuit. This method can be used to measure resistances quite accurately. The standard resistor should be 1% or better. When matching resistors, then it is just a case of observing the height of the trace for one resistor and then that for the other.

A dual-trace scope would make it easier, although a switch could be employed just as well to divert the probe of the scope from point A to point B. This would eliminate the need to move the probe back and forth.

## CHECKING SINGLE AND DUAL POTENTIOMETERS

A good potentiometer should track smoothly over its entire resistance range without sudden jumps and drops; a dual pot should track together (both sections equal) so that the

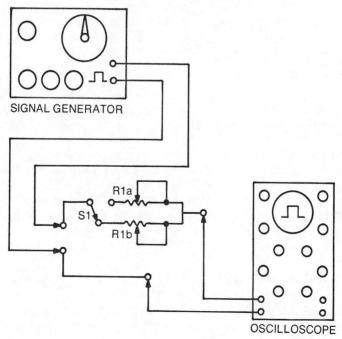

Checking single and dual pots

EQUIPMENT
SIGNAL GENERATOR.
POTENTIOMETER/S BEING TESTED.
OSCILLOSCOPE

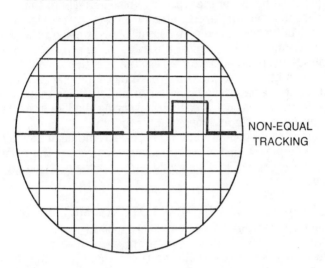

NON-EQUAL
TRACKING

.resistance in one pot is no more nor less than in the other.
There are circuits where a poorly working dual pot can upset
the circuit. For example, a dual volume control will throw the
balance of the speakers off if the gain from one channel of a
stereo amplifier is less or more than the gain of the other.

### Procedure

The audio generator should be set at any convenient
frequency. The output voltage should be high enough that the
resistance does not remove the trace from the face of the CRT.
The dual-trace scope is practically a must for this test. It
eliminates the need for a switch. Without the dual trace—one
for each section of the pot—flip the switch back and forth as
you slowly rotate the pot; the ganged pots are easier to check
since one knob controls both sections. As one flips back and
forth, the traces should always be equal in height. With a
single pot, slowly rotate it over its entire resistance range
while watching the trace. The switch in that case is
unnecessary.

### DETERMINING THE
### ACCURACY OF STEP ATTENUATORS

It is important to know whether a series of attenuators
follow an accurate ratio. This is true whether the attenuators

are part of an amplifier or those in the vertical input of an oscilloscope. A precise signal generator, whose output voltage is known to remain constant over its entire range, can quickly show the accuracy of the attenuators' ratios.

**Procedure**

If the attenuators being tested are part of the scope, then use the set up illustrated in Version 1. With the attenuators in another control circuit, a VTVM can be used instead, as in Version 2. In the case of the latter, a low output voltage should be set which can be read on the VTVM. Without changing any setting but that of the attenuators, read the ratio between the new reading and the old. Turn to the next step in the attenuator chain and do the same. Each step should exhibit the same difference from one setting to the next.

Where the scope's attenuators are in question, the method is very similar. Tune the signal generator to 60 Hz with the output voltage set at 0.01 volts. The scope's Vertical Gain Control is at "1". Adjust the gain so that the wave fills one division on the CRT. Change the setting to "10" and set the generator so it is producing 1 volt. The wave should be the same height as before. Do the same for each successive test. Although a slight difference may be seen, great changes

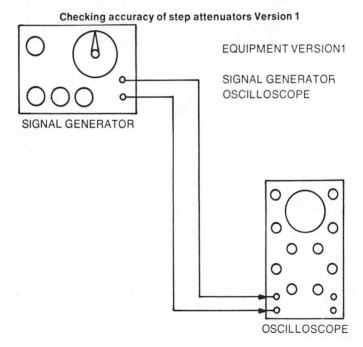

Checking accuracy of step attenuators Version 1

EQUIPMENT VERSION1

SIGNAL GENERATOR
OSCILLOSCOPE

SIGNAL GENERATOR

OSCILLOSCOPE

means the scope is not operating correctly and it should be repaired by a qualified technician. Some scopes do not have a series of steps, but use a pot for the control. With this arrangement, the pot can be calibrated for future use.

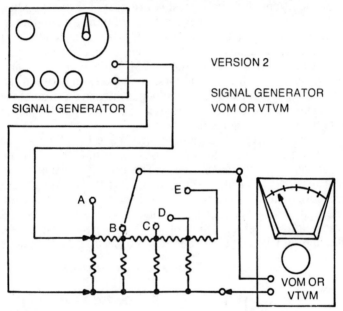

Checking accuracy of step attenuators Version 2

VERSION 2

SIGNAL GENERATOR
VOM OR VTVM

## CHECKING T-PADS

A T-pad is a combination of variable resistors used to attenuate a signal without changing the circuit impedance and without creating an observable amount of distortion. There are limits, however, to which a T-pad is subject. Beyond certain frequencies—this may be caused by the inherent design of the circuit, or in some cases due to the setting of the potentiometers which make up the T-pad—stray capacitances will bypass part of the AC voltage around the variable resistors. The test described will indicate exactly the points at which this occurs.

### Procedure

The output of the generator is connected to the T-pad circuit, which is terminated by resistors, $R1_z$ and $Ro_z$. Since T-pads may be audio or RF, depending on the circuit of which they are a part, the type signal generator must be matched to their usage. The generator is first tuned to a low frequency and then gradually swept upward. This sweeping may be done manually in the case of the RF or AF generator; with a sweep generator this function is accomplished automatically by the unit itself. The VTVM, whose probes are connected to the output of the T-pad circuit across $Ro_z$, is set to read a low AC voltage. At some point there will be a sharp deflection of the needle. Read the frequency on the generator's dial. This is the frequency at which the AC is bypassing the controls. The test should be repeated at various settings (high, medium and low) to see exactly how these settings actually affect the capacitative action of the T-pads. If it seems necessary, a graph can be drawn showing the complete action of the pots. This is usually more than necessary and becomes difficult unless the pots are calibrated.

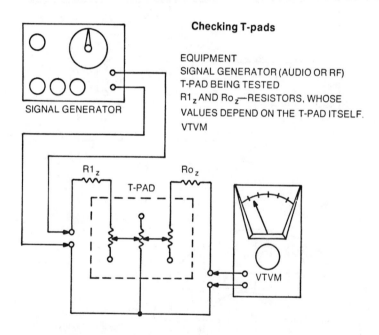

**Checking T-pads**

EQUIPMENT
SIGNAL GENERATOR (AUDIO OR RF)
T-PAD BEING TESTED
$R1_z$ AND $Ro_z$—RESISTORS, WHOSE VALUES DEPEND ON THE T-PAD ITSELF.
VTVM

SIGNAL GENERATOR

$R1_z$   $Ro_z$

T-PAD

VTVM

## CHECKING AND MATCHING CAPACITORS

This test can serve two purposes: it can be used to match capacitors, or it can be used to determine if two capacitors ostensibly of the same value are nevertheless so far apart in tolerance that they would upset a circuit which demands exact values. In the last case, one capacitor is used as the standard. The principle behind this test is that if the two capacitors

153

## Checking and matching capacitors

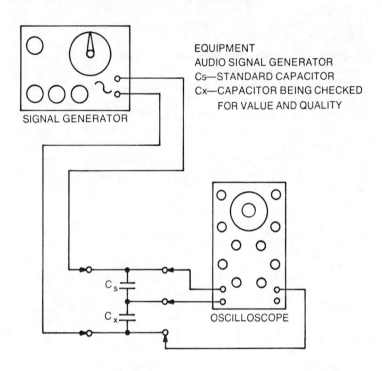

EQUIPMENT
AUDIO SIGNAL GENERATOR
Cs—STANDARD CAPACITOR
Cx—CAPACITOR BEING CHECKED
   FOR VALUE AND QUALITY

SIGNAL GENERATOR

$C_s$

$C_x$

OSCILLOSCOPE

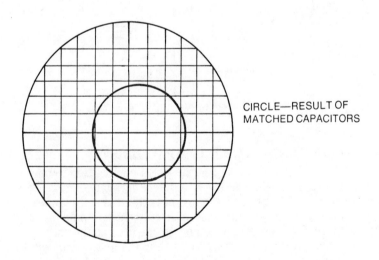

CIRCLE—RESULT OF
MATCHED CAPACITORS

match, the voltage and current at the vertical and horizontal inputs of the oscilloscope are 90 degrees apart.

## Procedure

The two capacitors are joined together and connected across the output of the signal generator. The generator should be set at an output voltage which must not be greater than the working voltage of the capacitors. The frequency is not of great importance; almost any range can be used. The hot lead of the generator goes to the V-input of the scope while the ground lead of the generator is connected to the H-input. If Cx has the same value as Cs, then a perfect circle will appear on the screen. If the capacitor is non-working, or has changed value, a series of small ellipses or lines will appear instead. However, if the sine wave is rich in harmonics some distortion will result. Nevertheless, when the two capacitors match, the circle—even with some distortion—will indicate that.

## CHECKING BYPASS CAPACITORS

Leaky or open bypass capacitors are often the cause of malfunctions in amplifiers, just as in radios and TV sets. However, they are often the last component to be checked,

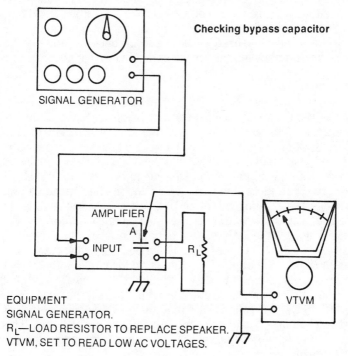

Checking bypass capacitor

SIGNAL GENERATOR

AMPLIFIER

A

INPUT

R_L

EQUIPMENT
SIGNAL GENERATOR.
$R_L$—LOAD RESISTOR TO REPLACE SPEAKER.
VTVM, SET TO READ LOW AC VOLTAGES.

VTVM

since they cause varied symptoms which are frequently not associated with the operation of the capacitor. When there is the least doubt about the poor operation of a bypass capacitor, check it to make certain the trouble does not originate there.

**Procedure**

Several frequencies should be injected into the circuit (at the appropriate level) either at the input or into the stage in question. The level in either case should be sufficient to drive the circuit to its full rated output. The VTVM is set at a range low enough so that small AC voltages can be observed. Place the probe from the VTVM at point A. A tiny voltage will probably be read on the meter. But an open capacitor will show up as a marked deflection on the meter. A scope can also be used as the terminating instrument to see whether any distortion is produced by this component.

## MEASURING SMALL CAPACITANCES

Although this method may not be used for measuring electrolytics, it offers a very simple way of measuring any small capacitance. The principle is that a known AC voltage from the signal generator is applied across the series-connected combination of known and unknown capacitors. A measured voltage is read and subtracted from the known voltage as produced by the signal generator. The ratio between measured voltage and produced voltage is the same as that between the known and unknown capacitors.

**Procedure**

The known capacitor, C1, should be a close tolerance unit, as the results of the measurement being no better than the tolerance of the capacitor. Its value can be around 0.01 $\mu$F. The output of the generator is connected to the two capacitors, C1 and the unknown, Cx. An AC VTVM is then connected across C1. The signal generator should be tuned to 1000 Hz at an output voltage which will give a good reading on the VTVM. A suggested reading might be five volts. With the setup as in the illustration, a reading is obtained on the VTVM of 3 volts. This would mean that the capacitance of the unknown capacitor is twice that of the known because when capacitors are in series, the applied voltage is divided among them—but in *inverse* proportion to its capacitance. This method will not give absolutely perfect answers, but in most circuit cases even a +80 and −20% tolerance capacitor may be acceptable. For greater accuracy, a capacitance checker would be better. This test as shown has the advantage of being simple and requiring no extra equipment.

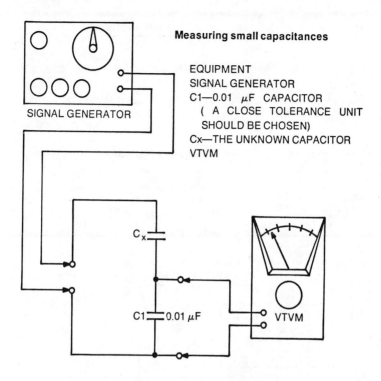

EQUIPMENT
SIGNAL GENERATOR
C1—0.01 $\mu$F CAPACITOR
( A CLOSE TOLERANCE UNIT
SHOULD BE CHOSEN)
Cx—THE UNKNOWN CAPACITOR
VTVM

## MEASURING CAPACITOR LEAKAGE

Knowing how much leakage an electrolytic capacitor is guilty of is more important than is commonly believed. The unit may look good, but the results will show up in a poorly working circuit, or one not working at all. The measurement is simple, since it consists merely of measuring the leakage current. The amount of tolerable leakage for various types of capacitors is as follows:

> Paper—0.9 mA per $\mu$F per volt
> Aluminum Foil—0.1 mA per $\mu$F per volt
> Tantalum—0.07 mA per $\mu$F per volt

### Procedure

The capacitor is inserted at terminals X and Y. Use any convenient output voltage from the generator which can be read on the VOM or VTVM. The meter is set to read DC current (which is leakage). Note how the capacitor is connected in the circuit. The frequency is unimportant. Once the current is read, it is applied to the equation:

$$\text{Leakage} = \frac{I \text{ (in mA)}}{\mu F \times E}$$

Although high leakage is a fault, beware on the other hand of a capacitor which shows no leakage at all. That means that the electrolytic has dried out and the capacitor should be thrown away.

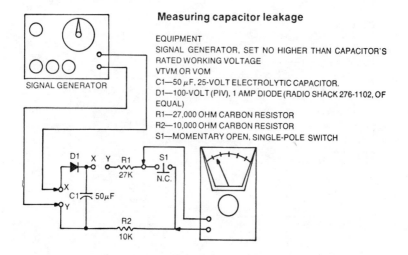

**Measuring capacitor leakage**

EQUIPMENT
SIGNAL GENERATOR, SET NO HIGHER THAN CAPACITOR'S RATED WORKING VOLTAGE
VTVM OR VOM
C1—50 $\mu$F, 25-VOLT ELECTROLYTIC CAPACITOR.
D1—100-VOLT (PIV), 1 AMP DIODE (RADIO SHACK 276-1102, OF EQUAL)
R1—27,000 OHM CARBON RESISTOR
R2—10,000 OHM CARBON RESISTOR
S1—MOMENTARY OPEN, SINGLE-POLE SWITCH

## MEASURING REACTANCE AND INDUCTANCE

A signal generator in association with a VTVM provides an excellent method for measuring reactance or inductance of a variety of components. Capacitors, coils and chokes all lend themselves to this type of measurement. This arrangement offers reasonable accuracy at audio and low radio frequencies. The principle involved is that the AC resistance across a potentiometer is equal to the reactance or impedance of a component being *checked within the same circuit.*

### Procedure

The output of the signal generator is connected to a very simple circuit consisting of a potentiometer, R1, and a switch with provisions for two jacks into which the component is attached. A sine wave of a low frequency (almost any within the range of 500 to 1000 Hz may be used) is passed through the circuit. Switch S1 permits alternately reading the resistance across the pot and then across the unknown. The pot is adjusted until its voltage drop is equal to the drop across the unknown component. This is done by flipping the switch from one position to the other. Once the two readings are exactly alike, take the pot out of the circuit and carefully measure the active part of the resistance which the pot placed into the circuit. This resistance is equal to the reactance of the component. If many components are to be checked, a semi-permanent arrangement of the circuit can be breadboarded, or for greater dependability wired together into a box. With a calibrated pot, there is then no need to take out the pot each time and measuring it. The reactance is read directly. A VOM can be used just as well as a VTVM.

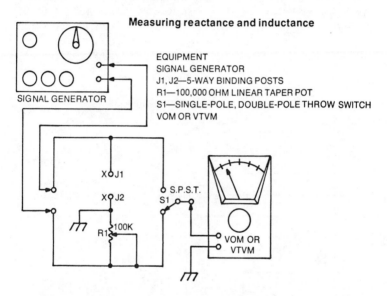

Measuring reactance and inductance

EQUIPMENT
SIGNAL GENERATOR
J1, J2—5-WAY BINDING POSTS
R1—100,000 OHM LINEAR TAPER POT
S1—SINGLE-POLE, DOUBLE-POLE THROW SWITCH
VOM OR VTVM

## MEASURING THE INDUCTANCE OF A COIL

Measuring the inductance of an unknown coil uses the same means as was employed in measuring capacitance. The equation used is:

$$L = \frac{X_L}{6.28 \ f}$$

L is inductance in henrys
$X_L$ is inductive reactance
f is frequency in hertz

We find the inductive reactance by comparing the resistance between the known resistor and the unknown inductor. We then solve the equation for the answer.

## Procedure

The output of the signal generator is set at 1 kHz or higher. In the case of small coils RF ranges must be used. The probe from the generator should then also be RF. With switch S1 in position 1, the unknown coil is removed from the circuit and only the resistor (a standard 1% unit of any value chosen which will cause the meter to read full scale), is read. The right hand side of the meter (the full scale reading) is the most accurate end of the meter. A digital meter does not have that disadvantage. When a satisfactory reading is obtained by manipulating the output from the signal generator, we then move the switch to position 2 so we are now reading voltage developed by the AC resistance of the coil. Once we have that figure, we substitute it in the equation shown above.

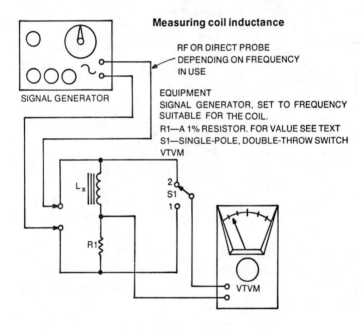

**Measuring coil inductance**

RF OR DIRECT PROBE DEPENDING ON FREQUENCY IN USE

EQUIPMENT
SIGNAL GENERATOR, SET TO FREQUENCY SUITABLE FOR THE COIL.
R1—A 1% RESISTOR. FOR VALUE SEE TEXT
S1—SINGLE-POLE, DOUBLE-THROW SWITCH
VTVM

## MEASURING INDUCTANCE OF AN RF COIL

With the aid of an RF generator, the inductance of unknown coils can be quickly found. Besides the generator, only a small wire loop and a close tolerance capacitor are required.

## Procedure

A good, high-dieletric, 100 pF capacitor is connected across the unknown coil. The generator is coupled to the circuit by way of a single turn loop. In some cases, if a reading cannot be obtained, use a two-turn loop instead. The VTVM is connected across the coil through its RF probe. Begin at the top of the generator's frequency range and tune downward until the resonant point is reached. This is indicated by a reading on the meter. Retune slowly to make certain of the exact frequency. This frequency (f) expressed in MHz is substituted in the following equation:

$$L \text{ (in microhenries)} = \frac{254}{F^2}$$

Although the capacitance of the probe has a loading factor, this can, in most cases, be ignored. The accuracy is almost entirely dependent on the capacitor, which means a close tolerance unit must be used.

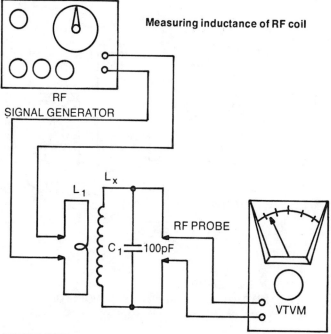

**Measuring inductance of RF coil**

EQUIPMENT

RF SIGNAL GENERATOR, SET AT HIGHEST RANGE AND THEN SWEPT DOWNWARDS.

C1—100 pF CAPACITOR, HIGH-DIELECTRIC CLOSE TOLERANCE.

L1—A ONE-TURN COIL.

$L_x$—COIL BEING MEASURED.

VTVM, SET TO READ DC VOLTAGE.

## CHECKING AUDIO OUTPUT TRANSFORMERS

Many output transformers come with several taps on the secondary. They may be 4, 8 and 16 ohms. However, there are times when either the tap is not labeled, or the speaker's impedance is unknown, or neither is known. A listening test by

**Checking audio output transformers**

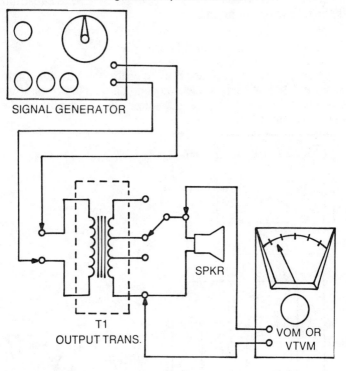

EQUIPMENT
AUDIO SIGNAL GENERATOR
OUTPUT TRANSFORMER
VOM OR VTVM, SET TO READ LOW AC VOLTAGE

trying one tap after another is not as conclusive as the method explained below. One's ears can be fooled and this is particularly true when the speaker's impedance may lie between two taps. Which of the two will sound better? By running the test explained as outlined here, a decision can be easily made.

### Procedure

Connect the signal generator to the primary of the audio output transformer. The generator should be tuned to about 1000 Hz with a low output voltage. One speaker lead is connected to the common or ground lead of the transformer, the other lead goes to one of the taps. The VOM or VTVM is connected directly across the speaker leads. Set the VOM so a reading is made in the center of the meter scale. Write down the value obtained with the speaker at one tap. Now move the hot lead to another tap and read that value. Check each tap the same way, making a note of the resulting voltage. The tap resulting in the highest reading is the one which most closely matches the impedance of the speaker. If several speakers are connected together, this test will show whether they should be in series or parallel and which tap is best for that group of speakers.

## MEASURING PHASE ANGLE OF THE INPUT IMPEDANCE OF A TRANSFORMER

When two signals are of the same frequency, a Lissajous figure on the oscilloscope can be used to determine the phase angle between the two signals. This is the principle employed in this test to determine the phase angle of the input impedance of a transformer.

### Procedure

In the illustration, we have the Lissajous pattern resulting from two signals (of the same frequency) 45 degrees apart. The phase angle has been determined by measuring the height of A from the X axis, then that of the distance of the highest point of the ellipse (which is B) measured also from the X axis. By dividing A by B, we get the sine of the angle. The output of the signal generator is tuned to any low frequency with an output voltage of no more than 1 volt rms. Note that the "hot" side of the H and V-inputs of the scope are tied together and the grounds are connected across the primary of the transformer under question. The frequency of the generator is tuned upward slowly. At the upper and lower limits of T1 the phase angle will be 45 degrees, resembling the illustration. At these two frequencies, the phase angle exists for the limits from which the input impedance is calculated. The resistors should be same impedance as the transformer primary and secondary.

## Measuring phase angle of input impedance of a transformer

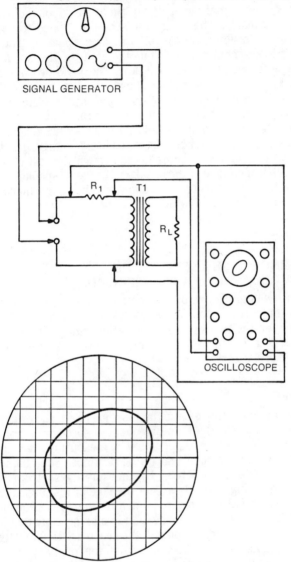

EQUIPMENT
AUDIO SIGNAL GENERATOR, SET AT A LOW FREQUENCY AND
SWEPT UPWARD.
R1—25 OHM, 2 WATT (OR MORE), RESISTOR.
R$_L$—RESISTOR LOAD FOR TRANSFORMER (APPROXIMATELY
100 OHMS).
T1—TRANSFORMER BEING CHECKED.

measuring phase angle of input impedance

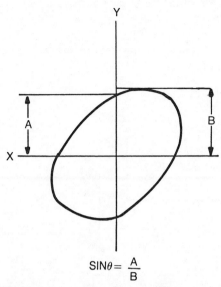

$$\text{SIN}\theta = \frac{A}{B}$$

## MEASURING TURNS RATIO OF A TRANSFORMER

An amplifier using a transformer in its output stage is subject to power losses and distortion if the correct impedance ratio is not maintained. When substituting a transformer, or designing one for a circuit, the proper turns ratio must be observed for proper functioning. The means of determining this are comparitively simple as the illustration shows.

### Procedure

Connect the output of the signal generator to the primary of the transformer. The frequency may be any tone that is within the expected operating range of the transformer, while the output voltage of the generator should be set as high as possible—say 10 volts. The VTVM or the VOM is set to read AC. First set the range switch on the multitester as its highest range, to avoid slamming the needle. Then, gradually work down until you are in the range at which a reading may easily be seen. The turns ratio is found by comparing voltage IN to voltage OUT.

In the equation:

$$\text{Turns ratio} = \sqrt{\frac{Z1}{Z2}}$$

165

where Z1 is usually the larger impedance and Z2 is the smaller. Since the voltage is dependent on the value of the impedance, a simple substitution provides a quick answer as to the turns ratio.

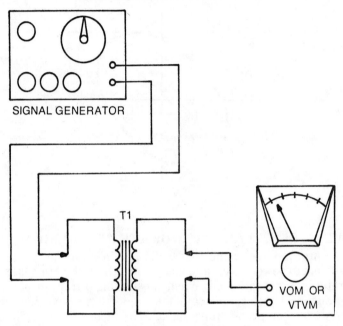

**Measuring turns ratio of transformer**

EQUIPMENT
SIGNAL GENERATOR
TRANSFORMER BEING MEASURED
VOM OR VTVM

## EVALUATING FREQUENCY RESPONSE
## OF A LOW-PASS FILTER

Usually a speech-clipper filter is set to obtain a cut-off point of about 2500 Hz when employed in the clipper's output circuit. But the question is: Is it? By using the setup shown below, the filter you are using can be judged as to whether that cut-off frequency is really being reached. If this test shows that a different cut-off point is reached, it is then a matter of changing the values of the coil and both capacitors until the desired point is reached.

## Procedure

The output of a signal generator is connected to the input of the low-pass filter. The generator range should be set to cover frequencies which will be above and below the 2500 Hz cut-off point, to make certain that you will reach that point as you sweep the generator. The resistor, R1, is chosen to provide an adequate output impedance to the VTVM. This value is usually about 600 ohms. As you turn up the generator frequency, watch the needle on the VTVM. As the cut-off point is reached, there will be a sharp deflection evident. That is the cut-off point of the filter and its actual frequency can be read from the generator's dial.

**Determining cut-off point of low-pass filter**

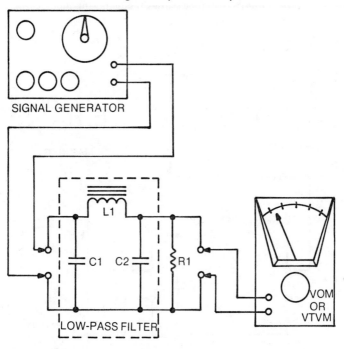

EQUIPMENT
 SIGNAL GENERATOR.
 CIRCUIT BEING CHECKED.
 R1—600 OHM RESISTOR (APPROXIMATELY)
 VTVM ( OR VOM, IF ITS IMPEDANCE IS HIGH ENOUGH NOT
TO UPSET THE CIRCUIT BEING CHECKED).

## MEASURING INDUCTANCE OF A
## COIL (SERIES RESONANT METHOD)

No component can be more useless than a coil whose inductance is unknown. In actuality, the test is simple and requires the simplest of test instruments. The technique is based on the principle that for a particular frequency, only one capacitance will resonate with an inductance. The reverse is also true: Any given inductance will resonate with only one capacitance at a specific frequency.

### Procedure

Connect the test circuit as shown. The capacitance of C1 should be in the same ball park as the unknown coil. Since that

**Measuring inductance (series resonance method)**

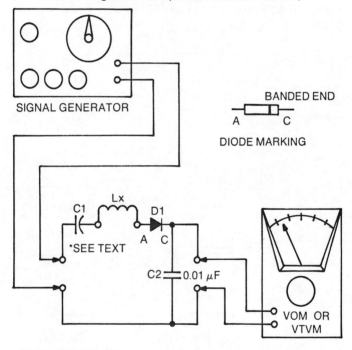

EQUIPMENT
    SIGNAL GENERATOR
    C1—SEE TEXT
    C2—0.01 $\mu$F PAPER TUBULAR CAPACITOR
    D1—CRYSTAL DIODE, TYPICALLY 1N50
    VTVM, OR VOM WITH AT LEAST 20,000
    OHMS/VOLT SENSITIVITY.

is a mystery, several capacitors may have to be tried. Set the generator to produce its maximum output—say 10 volts. The voltage developed across the series circuit is rectified by the diode. Set the VOM or VTVM to read DC volts at a low range. The tuning slug of the coil should be set at its maximum inductance. This is the center position of the tuning slug. The signal generator is varied across its range until the maximum deflection is observed on the meter. The highest peak is the resonant frequency of the circuit.

Knowing the frequency, the inductive reactance and the capacitive reactance can be calculated from the following two equations:

$$X_L = 2\pi fL$$

$$X_C = \frac{1}{2\pi fC}$$

At resonance both values will be equal, so we can rewrite the equations to:

$$L \times C = \frac{1}{(2\pi f)^2}$$

So, with the frequency you read on the generator's dial, the product of L and C is calculated and then divided by the known value.

## MEASURING HEADPHONE IMPEDANCE

Headphone impedances vary all over the lot. Quality has nothing to do with that measurement, but without knowing the impedance, a circuit can be loaded down by a pair of 8-ohm phones and the resulting sound level will be disappointing. Of course, if the circuit is designed for that impedance—then no trouble. To find the impedance of a particular set of phones, the setup shown will help to quickly furnish the answer. It should be remembered that impedance varies with frequency, so a tone of 1000 Hz has been chosen as the industry standard.

### Procedure

The resistor, R1, should be a close tolerance unit—1% or better; the tone is set at 1000 Hz at a level which will approximate an average listening sound. In some cases a worthwhile reading cannot be obtained, so instead use a 10 kHz tone. First the voltage drop is measured across the phones and then across the resistor by means of switch, S1. This switch is optional, but it helps to speed things up. By means of Ohm's Law, knowing the voltage drop and the current, the resistance (impedance) of the phones is easily found.

EQUIPMENT
AUDIO SIGNAL GENERATOR
R1—1000 OHM CARBON RESISTOR, 1% TOLERANCE OR
BETTER
S1—SINGLE-POLE, DOUBLE-POLE SWITCH (OPTIONAL)
HEADPHONES BEING CHECKED
VOM OR VTVM

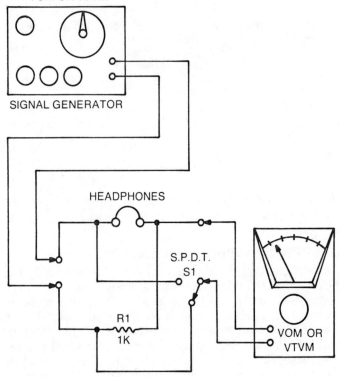

## DETERMINING THE FUNDAMENTAL
## FREQUENCY OF A CRYSTAL

A signal generator can be employed to determine the fundamental frequency of a crystal. The principle is that a meter will show a sharp deflection when the crystal resonates at its frequency as set by the signal generator.

### Procedure

A VOM with a minimum of 20,000 ohms-per-volt may be used for the meter, although a VTVM is better. If a VOM is used, an RF probe should be employed in conjunction with it.

The generator should cover the ranges from 30 kHz upwards. The coil used in the circuit should be about 100 $\mu$H. It can be made by winding a half-dozen turns around a half-inch form, although it is best to buy one ready made. Tune the signal generator to a frequency below the point at which you expect the crystal to resonate. As you tune the generator upwards, a point will be reached at which the needle on the meter will show a sharp deflection. This is the fundamental frequency of the crystal. As you continue upwards, there will be other points at which the meter will indicate a deflection. These are the odd harmonics—the third, fifth, etc. Be aware of these harmonics, as you may mistakenly take a reading for a harmonic and not the fundamental. The difference is acute; the fundamental

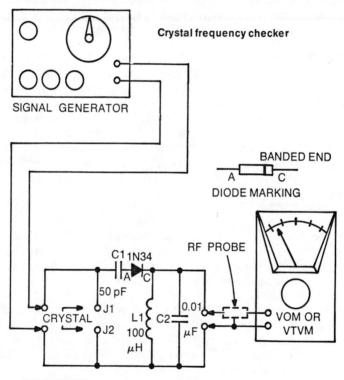

**Crystal frequency checker**

EQUIPMENT
RF SIGNAL GENERATOR.
VOM OR VTVM
C1—50 pF CAPACITOR
C2—0.01 $\mu$F DISC CERAMIC CAPACITOR
D1—ALMOST ANY SIGNAL TYPE DIODE (1N34, ETC.)
L1—100 $\mu$H COIL

frequency will result in a much more marked deflection than is the case with the harmonics. Once the fundamental frequency has been reached, it is read from the generator's dial. If many crystals are being checked, it becomes worthwhile to build the circuit inside a metal box and use 5-way binding posts for J1 and J2.

## DIODE IDENTIFYING CIRCUIT

What is that strange looking component? If it's a diode, is it a zener or a rectifier? Without markings on it which end is which? With the circuit described connected between your sine wave generator and a scope, your answers will come instantly. The theory behind the circuit is that you are applying a voltage across diode X to the horizontal terminals and a voltage representing current to the vertical terminals of the scope.

### Procedure

The generator should be set at its maximum voltage level. It should not be less than 10 volts. The frequency could be about 100 Hz. The amount of voltage applied to the circuit is determined by the potentiometer, R1. R3 limits the current to a safe level. R2 acts as a shunt to the vertical inputs. The diode, D1, indicates if the unknown diode is connected with the correct polarity. The reverse breakdown of most rectifier diodes cannot be determined, since there is only 10 volts present in the circuit.

The horizontal input selector should be set at "External Input." Reduce R1 until only a dot appears in the exact center of the CRT. Leave J1 and J2 open as you depress S1—a horizontal line will appear, while shorting the terminals together will produce a vertical line. This duplicates the effect of an open or shorted diode.

A rectifier diode connected across the terminals will show a straight horizontal line as you rotate R1. At one point the trace will make an abrupt vertical turn. If the diode was connected correctly as to polarity, the deflection will appear in the upper right hand section of the CRT. Reversed, the deflection will drop to the lower left hand side.

A zener is checked the same way except that its conduction curve is reversed as R1 is advanced. At one point, the trace will drop suddenly, which is the zener voltage point.

If the scope has been calibrated horizontally, it can be used to measure breakdown voltages of various diodes, provided they are less than the applied voltage.

**Diode identifying circuit**

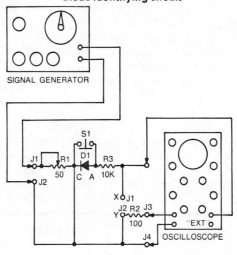

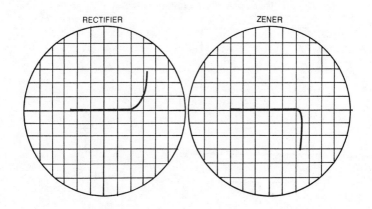

RECTIFIER ZENER

EQUIPMENT
   AUDIO SIGNAL GENERATOR
   OSCILLOSCOPE
   D1—30-VOLT (PIV) SILICON DIODE RECTIFIER (HEP 135
   OR EQUAL)
   J1, J2—5-WAY BINDING POTS
R1—50-OHM, 2WATT, LINEAR TAPER POTENTIOMETER
R2—100 OHM 1/2 WATT CARBON RESISTOR
R3—10,000 OHM 1/2 WATT CARBON RESISTOR
   S1—MOMENTARY OFF, SINGLE-POLE SWITCH
   J1, J2—5-WAY BINDING POST

## QUICK POLARITY AND CONTINUITY TESTER

An audio signal generator offers a quick way of checking the polarity of diodes, current gain of a transistor, or act as a continuity tester. The gain of a transistor will be only an approximation and not an actual measurement. But, if two transistors must be matched, their respective gains can be estimated closely enough for most purposes. The set-up shown is basically only a GO—NO—GO tester, but it has the advantage of being put together easily for the occasional test. It can also be breadboarded in minutes.

### Procedure

The signal generator is set to produce a frequency of approximately 100 Hz with an output voltage of 10 volts. If this is the maximum output voltage of the generator, it will not test high voltage diodes. The two LEDs and the resistor make up the whole circuit. R1 limits the current to a safe level. The generator is connected to J1 and J2, which can be any type of terminal; J3 and J4 can also be any type, although 5-way jacks are the most versatile. Note that J3 is marked *positive*. Place a diode between J3 and J4. Only one LED will light, since the

**Quick polarity & continuity tester**

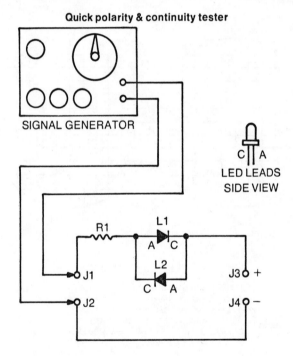

EQUIPMENT
SIGNAL GENERATOR
R1—270 OHM, 1-WATT RESISTOR.
L1, L2—LEDS (RADIO SHACK 276-042 OR EQUAL).
J1, 2, 3, 4—ANY TYPE OF TERMINAL OR CLIPS.

current flows in only one direction. If both LEDs illuminate, the diode is shorted. Only two terminals of a transistor are connected. Which LED lights will depend on the polarity of the transistor or diode being inserted.

## CURVE TRACING WITH A GENERATOR

What is that strange looking component? If it's a diode, is it a zener or a rectifier? Without markings on it, which end is which? With the circuit shown connected between your sine wave generator and a scope, the answer will come quickly. The theory behind the circuit is that you are applying a voltage which is across the diode X to the horizontal terminal and a voltage representing current to the vertical terminal of the scope. Transistor and capacitors will reveal their secrets also.

### Procedure

The generator should be set at its maximum output range. This is usually about 10 volts. This means that the under-test zeners' breakdown voltage must be below that figure. The frequency can be set for 100 Hz, although that is not important. The amount of voltage applied to the circuit is determined by the potentiometer, R1. R3 limits the current to a safe level, allowing you to test most semiconductors in-circuit.

The scope Horizontal Input selector is set at "External Input." Reduce R1 until only a dot appears in the exact center of the CRT. Leave J1 and J2 open as you depress S1— a horizontal line will appear. Shorting the terminals together will produce a vertical line. This duplicates the effect of an open or shorted diode.

A rectifier diode connected across the terminals will show a straight horizontal line as you rotate R1. At one point the trace will make an abrupt vertical turn. If the diode was connected properly as to polarity, the deflection will appear in the upper right hand section of the CRT. Reversed, the deflection will drop instead to the lower left hand side.

A zener is checked the same way except that its conduction curve is reversed as R1 is advanced. At one point the trace will drop suddenly, which is the zener's breakdown point...if it is within the generator's limit.

If the scope has been calibrated horizontally, it can be used to measure exact breakdown voltages of various diodes, provided they are rated at less than the applied voltage.

A good capacitor connected across J1 and J2 will cause an ellipse to form. An in-circuit transistor can be checked through junction operation by noting the discontinuity, typically seen at the zero junction.

## Curve tracing of semiconductors

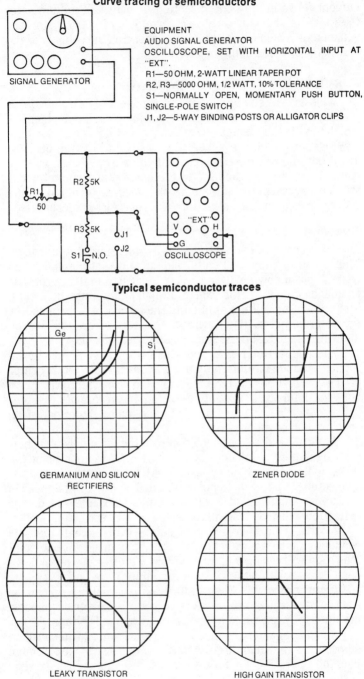

EQUIPMENT
AUDIO SIGNAL GENERATOR
OSCILLOSCOPE, SET WITH HORIZONTAL INPUT AT "EXT".
R1—50 OHM, 2-WATT LINEAR TAPER POT
R2, R3—5000 OHM, 1/2 WATT, 10% TOLERANCE
S1—NORMALLY OPEN, MOMENTARY PUSH BUTTON, SINGLE-POLE SWITCH
J1, J2—5-WAY BINDING POSTS OR ALLIGATOR CLIPS

SIGNAL GENERATOR

R1 50

R2 5K

R3 5K

S1 N.O.

J1

J2

"EXT"

V   H

G

OSCILLOSCOPE

## Typical semiconductor traces

Ge   Si

GERMANIUM AND SILICON RECTIFIERS

ZENER DIODE

LEAKY TRANSISTOR

HIGH GAIN TRANSISTOR

176

## TRANSISTOR CURVE TRACER

Combining a sweep generator with a scope, plus a few assorted components, will yield an excellent transistor curve

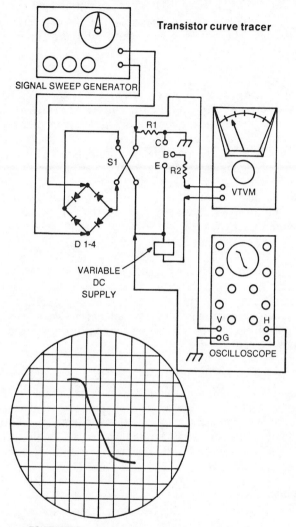

**Transistor curve tracer**

EQUIPMENT
AUDIO OR SWEEP SIGNAL GENERATOR.
D1-D4—FULL WAVE BRIDGE RECTIFIER (RADIO SHACK 276-1151, OR EQUAL).
S1—DOUBLE-POLE, DOUBLE-THROW SWITCH, BREAK BEFORE MAKE SWITCH.
R1—1000 OHM CARBON RESISTOR.
P—VARIABLE DC POWER SUPPLY.
VOM, SET TO READ CURRENT.

tracer. The unit will provide the entire family of traces you need to find out what a particular transistor will do. It can also be used for checking other semiconductors. With it, curve tracing for either NPN or PNP units are carried out easily. It is a more complex circuit to assemble than the in-circuit tester described elsewhere in this book, but it will offer many more parameters.

### Procedure

If the sweep generator you have available has a capacitatively coupled output, the full-wave bridge rectifier must be used to provide a completely symmetrical load to the generator. The latter is set at a frequency of 60-Hz with an output of 10 volts. The polarity of the applied DC voltage is reversed by means of S1, so that both types of transistors can be checked. In the position as shown in the illustration, the collector is negative while positive voltage is on the emitter. The bias voltage, B1, is varied to adjust the current across the base, which is measured by the VOM in the current reading mode. By varying the value of the base current, all of the important traces can be obtained.

To find what the traces should look like for every type of parameter, the manufacturer's spec sheets should be obtained. If this is not possible, take a known good transistor and observe the trace you obtain when you run the tests shown above. Then compare these traces with those from the questionable semiconductor.

### CHECKING IN-CIRCUIT TRANSISTORS

There is no need to unsolder a transistor to find out if it is operating correctly. There is always the danger that unsoldering a transistor can damage a perfectly good unit. Instead, by using the arrangement shown, probably a dozen transistors can be checked in less time than it takes to unsolder just one.

### Procedure

The output of the signal generator is connected via a direct probe to the input of a typical transistor stage as shown. Set the generator at about 400 Hz, with a very low output voltage. Remember that a continuous tone can overload a stage at an otherwise safe level, such as from musical peaks. A small blocking capacitor should be connected between the generator and the transistor, if one is not already in the circuit you are testing. The sine wave is applied to the base of the transistor and this voltage is measured by the VTVM (or VOM) by placing the switch in position 1. By moving the switch to position 2, you are now reading the voltage obtained from the collector. The beta of the transistor is the ratio of this tiny change in collector current to the change in base current, provided there is no change in collector voltage. If the beta obtained differs remarkably from the spec sheet, then the transistor is not "up to snuff." One point should be remembered: if the voltage is measured by a VOM, make certain that it has a very high impedance input or the circuit will be loaded down, producing erroneous results.

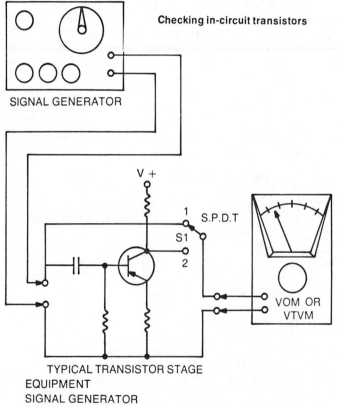

Checking in-circuit transistors

TYPICAL TRANSISTOR STAGE
EQUIPMENT
SIGNAL GENERATOR
CIRCUIT BEING TESTED.
S1—SINGLE-POLE, DOUBLE-THROW
VTVM OR VOM

## CHECKING PHOTOCELL FREQUENCY RESPONSE

A photocell, whether it be silicon or selenium, exhibits different responses based on the excitation light modulations.

To find the peak energy output, the arrangement shown is a relatively simple way of determining that response. The principle is that the LED is modulated by the amplifier's output, the response being displayed on the scope.

## Procedure

The signal generator may produce a triangle or square wave, the type of wave being unimportant. The frequency to which the generator is tuned should be just below the expected response range of the photocell. The cell is mounted in a light-tight enclosure with the LED. The output of the generator is connected to the input of an audio amplifier whose output modulates the cell with the aid of biasing battery B1. R2 is a terminating resistor suitable for the output of the cell. The oscilloscope then displays the trace which is obtained with the aid of biasing battery B2. The cell will distort the waveform, but at some frequency, which is arrived at by slowly tuning the generator upwards, a sharp cut-off point will be visible on the scope. This is the limit of the photocell's frequency response. It is important that the frequencies being used are within the amplifier's range, or the cut-off point will be that of the amplifier and not that of the cell.

**Checking photocell's frequency response**

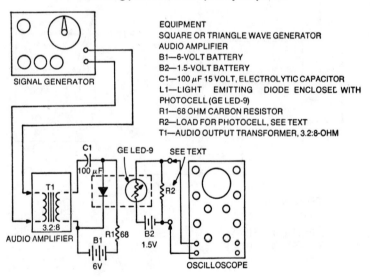

EQUIPMENT
SQUARE OR TRIANGLE WAVE GENERATOR
AUDIO AMPLIFIER
B1—6-VOLT BATTERY
B2—1.5-VOLT BATTERY
C1—100 $\mu$F 15 VOLT, ELECTROLYTIC CAPACITOR
L1—LIGHT EMITTING DIODE ENCLOSED WITH PHOTOCELL (GE LED-9)
R1—68 OHM CARBON RESISTOR
R2—LOAD FOR PHOTOCELL, SEE TEXT
T1—AUDIO OUTPUT TRANSFORMER, 3.2:8-OHM

SIGNAL GENERATOR

C1
100 $\mu$F
GE LED-9
SEE TEXT
R2
T1
3.2:8
AUDIO AMPLIFIER
B1
R1 68
B2
1.5V
6V
OSCILLOSCOPE

# Chapter 7

# Testing Audio
# Amplifiers and Speakers

Hi-fi sets, stereos, quadraphonic systems, or "sound machines"—by whatever name, are not only a part of the current scene these days—they are also fundamentally the same—composed of audio amplifiers and speakers. Therefore, the same basic techniques can be employed to check their proper operation. Following are many methods, using a signal generator, which can be used to quickly check if a particular system is operating up to par.

## CHECKING OVERDRIVE DISTORTION
## OF A SPEECH AMPLIFIER

When a speech amplifier, or for that matter, any amplifier is fed a signal which is too strong to be handled well, that is, it is overdriven—distortion results. There are several tests to determine if that sad state exists, but the one shown here requires only an oscilloscope.

### Procedure

Connect the output of an audio signal generator to the input of the speech amplifier. Terminate the amplifier with a dummy load, represented as $R_L$. This resistor should equal the usual termination value. The vertical inputs of the scope are connected across the terminating resistor. The H-input is connected to the hot side of the signal generator. The SYNC sweep on the scope is set to EXT. The generator is set at some mid-range frequency within the speech spectrum; 800 to 2000 Hz would be approximately correct. Since the H and V-inputs of the scope are fed the same voltage and frequency, a straight line should result. However, this is true only if the amplifier is NOT overdriven. When it is, there will be flattening of the line at both ends as shown in the illustration. Even the best of amplifiers under the best of conditions will show some of this flattening, but it should be kept to an irreducible minimum.

**Checking overload distortion on ham set**

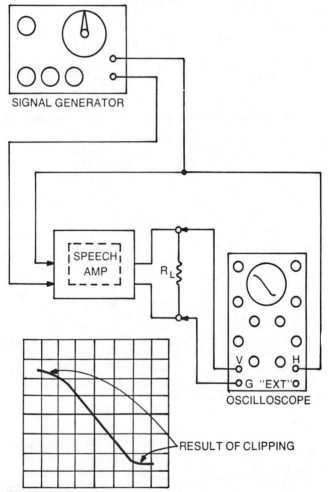

EQUIPMENT
SIGNAL GENERATOR.
AMPLIFIER BEING TESTED.
$R_L$—RESISTOR EQUAL IN VALUE TO THE IMPEDANCE OF THE SPEAKER IT IS REPLACING.
OSCILLOSCOPE.

## CHECKING THE LINEARITY OF AN AUDIO AMPLIFIER

The linearity of an audio amplifier is simple to check—provided, however, you are certain of the linearity of the oscilloscope's own amplifiers. Checking the latter is explained in the section under Scopes. This test will not only reveal the non-linearity of an audio amplifier, but will indicate when the amplifier becomes overloaded.

### Procedure

Connect the output of the signal generator to the input of the amplifier being tested. Its output is connected to the input of the scope, which is joined across the load resistor. A resistor equal in value to the speaker it is replacing is better for many tests, since a speaker may introduce distortion which could reflect on the amplifier. The hot lead of the generator is also connected to the horizontal input of the scope. The signal generator may be a sine, square, or triangle waveform generator. The actual waveform is unimportant, since all we want to find out is if the amplifier is capable of producing a straight line trace on the CRT. First, allow a warm-up period for the scope and for the generator. This precaution is true for any test which involves tube equipment. Five minutes is not

**Checking linearity of an audio amplifier**

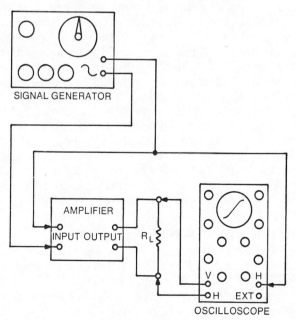

EQUIPMENT

SIGNAL GENERATOR
AMPLIFIER BEING TESTED
$R_L$—RESISTOR EQUAL IN VALUE TO THE IMPEDANCE OF THE
SPEAKER IT IS REPLACING
OSCILLOSCOPE

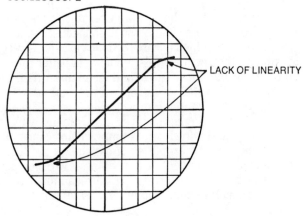

LACK OF LINEARITY

too much. In the case of solid state equipment, a couple of minutes should give the transistors time to arrive all at the same temperature. Almost any frequency can be set for the generator—400 Hz and upward—as long as it is within the amplifier's capability to handle. The scope horizontal selector should be at "External." By adjusting the horizontal and vertical gain controls, a 45 degree line should be obtained. If the line is perfectly straight, then the amplifier is linear and is not suffering from overloading. Otherwise, there will be a leveling off at either or at both ends, of the line as shown. In other words, the line may be straight, but as you begin to increase the output voltage of the generator, you will also see this leveling-off effect. Be careful that you do not cause the transistors to burn out when increasing the input voltage.

## MEASURING SENSITIVITY OF AN AMPLIFIER

This is another test which is necessary to fully know the capabilities of an amplifier. The terminating instrument can be a VOM, provided it has a high enough impedance, so as not to load down the circuit under test. A VTVM is better, due to its high impedance, if one is handy.

### Procedure

Connect the units as shown in the sketch. R1 is a load resistor equal to the impedance of the speaker, usually 4 or 8 ohms. Its power rating must be at least equal to the full power output of the amplifier. While it is true that a speaker can be connected at the output for such a test, it may add complications. The test requires running the amplifier at full output and one must be careful because a steady tone at that level may destroy the speaker's cone. The generator is tuned to 400 Hz with a voltage output sufficient to drive the amplifier to full output. The input voltage is read in rms and the other measurement is read as the power across R1 determined by the equation:

$$P = \frac{E^2}{R}$$

**Measuring input sensitivity of amplifier**

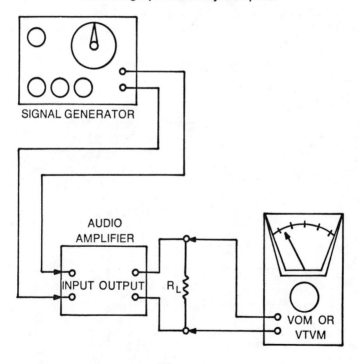

### MEASURING MAXIMUM INPUT SIGNAL LEVEL

Too low an input signal as seen by an amplifier results in an output below its rated specs. Conversely, too high can result in distortion. To avoid one or the other, it becomes necessary to know the correct input signal, if it is not otherwise available. To acertain the exact value, the set up described here allows a quick method of measurement.

**Procedure**

The correct impedance load should be selected to match the amplifier's input. Although waveform can be used, a triangle wave is preferable in the author's estimation. A square wave can also be employed as can a sine wave. In the use of the latter, a fairly high percentage of distortion must be present before it is visible on the scope. The triangle wave is much clearer in that sense. First check the waveform available from your signal generator by means of S1, which bypasses the amplifier entirely. It should not be forgotten that a generator or the leads can cause distortion and it should be recognized before beginning the measuring. Set the generator at 400 or 1000 Hz. Actually, any frequency can be chosen, provided it is within the amplifier's range. Begin with a signal in which the resulting output is barely read on the scope.

Measuring maximum input signal level

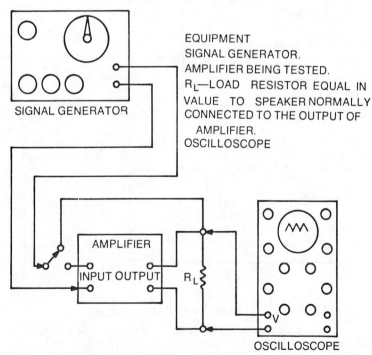

EQUIPMENT
SIGNAL GENERATOR.
AMPLIFIER BEING TESTED.
$R_L$—LOAD RESISTOR EQUAL IN VALUE TO SPEAKER NORMALLY CONNECTED TO THE OUTPUT OF AMPLIFIER.
OSCILLOSCOPE

SIGNAL GENERATOR

AMPLIFIER
INPUT OUTPUT $R_L$

OSCILLOSCOPE

Slowly increase the signal (which should be in the millivolt range) until distortion appears. Now back down the output until the distortion has disappeared. When a clean signal is apparent, read the output on the generator's meter. If the generator is not provided with one, read the output level with the VTVM.

## DETERMINING SQUARE WAVE RESPONSE OF AN AMPLIFIER

Square waves offer certain advantages in discovering the distortion and of what type that exists in an amplifier, or for that matter, any circuit. The setup illustrated here will allow you to examine any circuit whose response is in question. The square wave is rich in harmonics. A sine wave is a "pure" tone with only its fundamental tone. A square wave consists not only of the fundamental, but also of the odd harmonics. If a 400 Hz tone is injected into a scope, the resulting trace consists of the fundamental, the third, fifth, seventh as well as the ninth harmonics. Which means that a 400 Hz tone also contains a 1200, 2000, 2800 and 3600 Hz tones up to 10 times its fundamental.

In actual practice a 2 kHz tone will test a circuit up to 20 kHz. Although this is above the limits of human hearing, square wave generators are able to go much above that. Even if they cannot be heard, the harmonics add much to the richness of the fundamental tones. And high frequency distortion will distort the audible tones.

### Procedure

Resistor R1 is a load which replaces the speaker, or the speakers themselves can be left in the circuit. Begin with a 50 Hz tone and bypass the amplifier with S1. This allows the square wave to be examined on the scope. Make certain your generator or the probe is not causing distortion of its own. Switch the amplifier into the circuit and begin the tests. There is no such thing as a circuit without some distortion. Even a piece of straight wire has some—it can pick up hum. So, do not be disappointed when first viewing the trace on the scope. The degree of distortion and what type is important. Note the examples of scope traces in the illustration. In some cases, the very design of the circuit could be at fault. In others, the distortion can be cured with simple adjustments. After each adjustment, check the result to make sure the adjustments are in the right direction. Of course, it must be understood that a broad range of tones must be injected into the amplifier and each tone checked on the scope.

**Determining square waves response of amplifier**

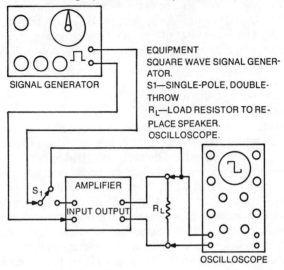

EQUIPMENT
SQUARE WAVE SIGNAL GENER-
ATOR.
S1—SINGLE-POLE, DOUBLE-
THROW
$R_L$—LOAD RESISTOR TO RE-
PLACE SPEAKER.
OSCILLOSCOPE.

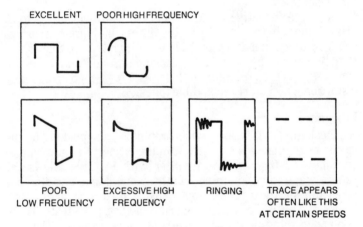

## MEASURING FREQUENCY RESPONSE OF A CIRCUIT

It is often necessary to know the extent of the "flatness" of an amplifier, preamp or filter circuits. This information is as important as the overall ability of the circuit to handle a broad range of tones. With the setup illustrated, it becomes a simple process of plotting the points which indicate the output in relation to the frequency. Once these points are determined and marked on a sheet of log graph paper, a line is drawn joining the points together to form an understandable curve.

**Plotting frequency response of a circuit**

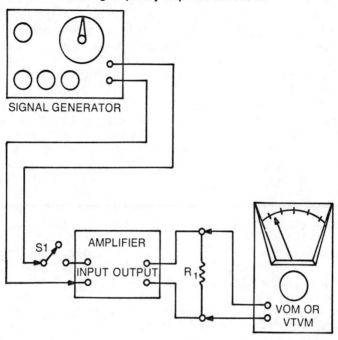

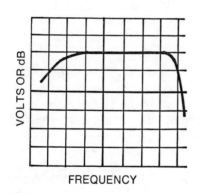

FREQUENCY

EQUIPMENT
AUDIO SIGNAL GENERATOR.
S1—SINGLE-POLE, DOUBLE-THROW
R1—EQUAL IN OHMS TO IMPEDANCE OF OUTPUT CIRCUIT.
VOM OR VTVM, SET TO AC VOLTS.
AMPLIFIER BEING MEASURED.

### Procedure

An audio sine wave generator is connected to the circuit under test. Make certain that the circuit is terminated with the proper load. An amplifier must be "loaded" with a resistor which is equal to the impedance of the speaker normally used—4 or 8 ohms and which is also equal to the rated output of the amplifier in watts.

The output of the signal originating in the generator should be of a sufficient level to drive the circuit to its rated output. Once that level is set, it should remain the same for the balance of the tests. It is taken for granted that the signal generator has a constant output over its entire frequency range. If not, the curve will reflect the level of the generator and not that of the amplifier.

The level should first be measured on the VTVM. Apply a signal whose frequency is as low as the circuit under test is capable of handling. Now move the switch, S1, to include the amplifier in the circuit. The graph paper should be marked (as in the sample) with frequency in Hz on one axis and the output—expressed in volts or in dBs—on the other. Move to the next frequency and repeat the process. The more points chosen and the closer the frequencies, the more complete the curve will be. Continue until the point is reached beyond which the circuit will not pass those frequencies.

If you own or can borrow a sweep generator, manual plotting is eliminated since the envelope of the wave, as reproduced on the scope, gives an instant picture of the flatness of the output levels.

### MEASURING OUTPUT IMPEDANCE OF AN AMPLIFIER

Although this test is designed to measure the output impedance of an amplifier, it can be used for any circuit whose impedance needs to be known. It can be employed with a preamp or any control circuit.

### Procedure

The output of the signal generator is connected to the input of the amplifier under test. Direct probes are used in this case. The output of the amplifier should be terminated with a variable resistor, R1, whose value is known to be much larger than the impedance of the circuit being tested. The generator should produce a 1000 Hz tone at any output voltage which will cause the meter to deflect to almost full scale. Use switch S1 to measure the voltage drop when the pot is in the circuit. Now adjust the pot until its resulting voltage reading is exactly half that of the amplifier reading. Then, it is simply a matter of measuring the active part of the resistance which gives that one-half reading. That resistance is measured by taking the pot out of the circuit and without disturbing it, measuring that resistance. This is equal to the output impedance of the circuit under test.

**Measuring output impedance of amplifier**

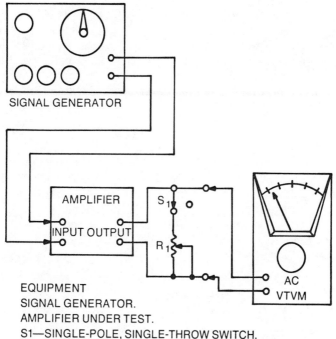

EQUIPMENT
SIGNAL GENERATOR.
AMPLIFIER UNDER TEST.
S1—SINGLE-POLE, SINGLE-THROW SWITCH.
R1—SEE TEXT.
AC VTVM.

## MEASURING THE POWER OUTPUT OF AN AUDIO AMPLIFIER

The power output of an amplifier, either as part of a radio or a TV receiver, or as a separate audio component, can be very simply measured with the set-up shown below. The voltage is measured with the aid of a signal generator, and the power output is then calculated by means of the following equation:

$$P_o = \frac{V_o{}^2}{Z}$$

Where: $p_o$ is power output
Z is the impedance of the speaker
$V_o$ is the output voltage

## Procedure

An audio signal capable of driving the amplifier is applied to its input. The VTVM or VOM is adjusted to read AC voltage. The volume control of the amp is turned all the way up. The output voltage is then read across the voice coil. When dealing with extremely high-powered units, a resistance load equal to the speaker impedance should be substituted to avoid possible damage to the speaker. Once the reading is obtained, the figure is placed in the equation.

Assuming that the output voltage was 40 and the speaker impedance was 8, the equation now reads:

$$P_o = \frac{40^2}{8} = 200 \text{ Watts}$$

Since this is the result of applying only one frequency, the generator should be tuned to other frequencies within the range of the amplifier to obtain a better overall picture of the unit's performance.

**Measuring power output of an amplifier**

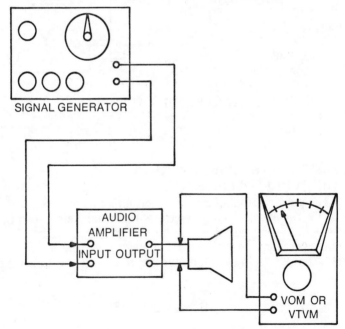

## CHECKING AMPLIFIER FOR FREQUENCY DISTORTION

Frequency distortion is caused by the amplifier's inability to amplify all of the frequencies found in the input signal at the same ratio. Although this type of distortion is usually subtle, it can make an amplifier "hard to listen to." To determine whether this is present, all that is necessary is a signal generator and an oscilloscope. The arrangement shown below indicates if this form of distortion is present, to what degree it exists, and in which frequency band. It is to be expected that a PA amplifier cannot handle upper range frequencies as can a hi-fi unit.

### Procedure

Connect an audio signal generator to the amplifier's input. The output voltage should be no more than is necessary to produce full output. A load resistor matching the impedance of the speaker is substituted for it. The output is connected to the scope by means of a direct probe. It is better to use DC coupling on the scope for the low frequencies. Slight or no

**Checking amplifier for frequency distortion**

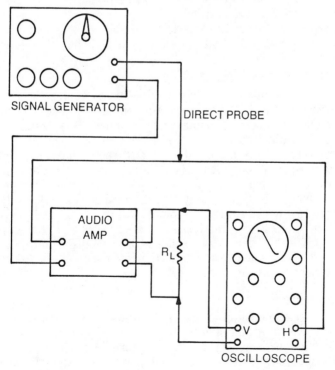

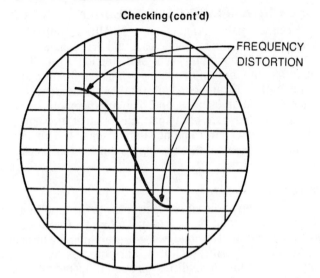

FREQUENCY
DISTORTION

distortion will be represented by an ellipse or a diagonal line which will be quite crisp on the screen. The figure will become blurred or bent out of shape when amplifier distortion is present in great quantities. The scope shows a trace indicating frequency distortion; this is noticeable at both ends of the diagonal line, which instead of being straight has become bent.

## CHECKING IM DISTORTION

This is a test of importance to the audiophile. IM, or intermodulation distortion, is caused by one or more frequencies being modulated by another. This destroys the relationship, which should remain constant over the entire audio spectrum, among the various frequencies which make up music. Although it is of less importance in a PA amplifier, which is concerned only with voice, even there it can be annoying. Today, so many offices and plants have PA systems through which music is piped in, that IM must not be overlooked there. The test illustrated below will give only an approximate idea of the existence of IM. A distortion analyzer would be needed to measure the exact amount of distortion present in any given unit.

### Procedure

Use the hookup as shown. First observe the waveform of one generator and then the other. This is to make certain that they are both generating an undistorted waveform. To begin the test, both generators should be set to the same frequency

**Checking IM distortion**

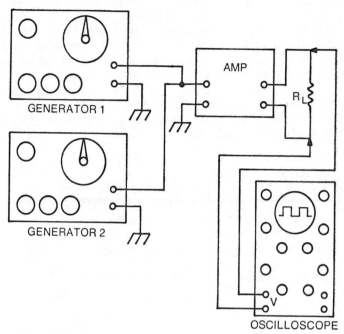

EQUIPMENT
TWO SIGNAL GENERATORS.
AMPLIFIER UNDER TEST.
$R_L$—LOAD RESISTOR.
OSCILLOSCOPE.

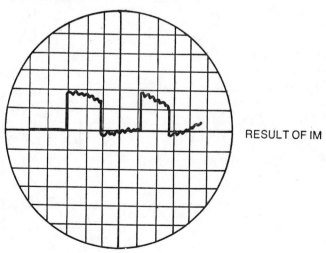

RESULT OF IM

that is within the generator's limits. Then turn up one generator, keeping the other to the original frequency. Watch the results on the scope. At one point, if IM is present, the scope will show a trace similar to the one illustrated. The scope will indicate roughly how much distortion exists and the dials of the generator will reveal at what frequencies this distortion is taking place. If IM is caused by poor design, which is often the case, there is obviously nothing much that can be done except get another, and hopefully a better unit. Tests can be run on the individual transistors or tubes since they, too, can be the cause of IM.

## CHECKING STEREO AMPLIFIER'S SQUARE WAVE RESPONSE

A stereo amplifier or preamplifier offers an advantage when testing: one channel can be compared to the other. This works only if one channel is obviously working better than the other. If one channel is to be used as a standard, then it is

**Checking stereo amp for square wave response**

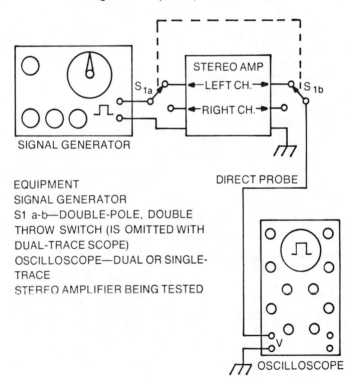

EQUIPMENT
SIGNAL GENERATOR
S1 a-b—DOUBLE-POLE, DOUBLE
THROW SWITCH (IS OMITTED WITH
DUAL-TRACE SCOPE)
OSCILLOSCOPE—DUAL OR SINGLE-
TRACE
STEREO AMPLIFIER BEING TESTED

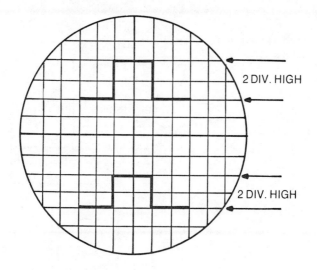

2 DIV. HIGH

2 DIV. HIGH

important that first you have made certain the better of the two is operating close to what it should, otherwise the test would have no value. A square wave is used for this test, since this wave covers frequencies up to ten times that of the fundamental tone.

**Procedure**

A dual-trace oscilloscope is a decided advantage when conducting this test, but the switch as shown in the illustration allows comparison between one channel and the other. Tone controls should be at their "flat" settings for both channels. In many cases, treble and bass controls affect the waveform and would provide incorrect and spurious waveforms. Turn the switch from one position to the other while noticing if there are observable changes. Measure the amplitude of the waveforms for both channels using the "good" channel for a reference. Check the corners of the square wave to see if one channel has more distortion than the other and in which frequency band. Test with the tone controls in other positions, making certain that they are at the same setting for both channels. There should be little difference between the two channels.

**CHECKING PHASE RELATIONSHIP**

Phase relationship, like a personal relationship, can be good or bad. It can improve the characteristics of an amplifier, or it can cause it to go into oscillation. Negative feedback is one in which part of the output signal is returned to

197

**Checking phase relationship**

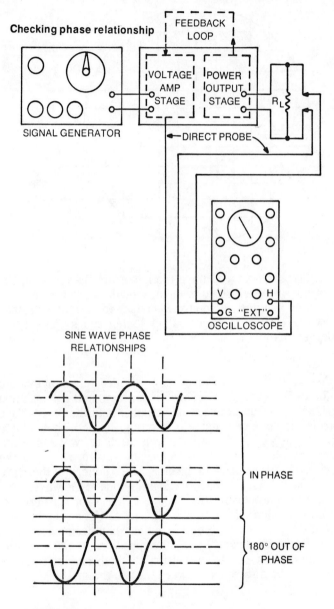

EQUIPMENT
AUDIO SIGNAL GENERATOR OR SWEEP GENERATOR.
AMPLIFIER UNDER TEST.
OSCILLOSCOPE, SET TO READ "EXT" ON HORIZONTAL CONTROL.
R_L—DUMMY LOAD, AS EXPLAINED IN TEST.

the input, but 180 degrees out of phase. (See the illustration.) While negative feedback acts as a reverse bias, limiting the output of the amplifier, it provides stabilization. It is important that all of the frequencies be 180 degrees out of phase which the amplifier is expected to handle. If this is not the case, distortion results. Positive feedback converts the amplifier into an oscillator, as was explained in Chapter 1 of the book. The test outlined below will indicate where and to what degree phase shift exists.

### Procedure

An audio generator can do this test, if a sweep generator is not available. The latter avoids the need for repeated testing over numerous frequencies to get an overall picture. The sweep generator does it at once. Make certain that the input of the amplifier is not overloaded. Feed a signal from the generator (which is no more than is needed) to drive the amplifier to full output. Use a dummy load (a resistor) which is of the value of the speaker's impedance (4 or 8 ohms are typical). The amplifiers output is connected to the vertical inputs of the scope. The horizontal input leads of the scope go to the input stage of the amplifier. We are now ready to observe the phase relationship. What we are trying to find is if the two waveforms are starting at the same time. If they are we can say that frequency, or frequencies, are in phase. A 180-degree phase shift, which is the ideal, will be observed as a straight line on the CRT from the upper left hand quadrant of the tube angling downward at 45 degrees to the lower right hand quadrant.

## MEASURING GAIN (VOLTS OR DB) OF AN AMPLIFIER

To know if an amplifier or a preamp is doing what it should—amplifying, a quick test is to measure the signal voltage in and the voltage out. The ratio, either in dB or in volts, is then calculated easily. Such a test offers a simple but effective method of getting the overall picture of the unit's operation. With a stereo amplifier, one can compare the gain of one channel as against the gain of the other, provided that one channel is known to be up to specs.

### Procedure

It is important that distortion is not introduced during the course of the test. If it is, the resulting ratio will prove nothing. Consequently, care should be taken that once the amplifier is connected as in the illustration, the output voltage of the generator is no more than is needed to drive the amplifier to full output—AND NO MORE. First, set the generator at about 1000 Hz, observing the precautions mentioned above. The probe of the VTVM should be of the demodulator type to avoid loading down the circuit. The voltage (or dB) into the amp is read from the generator's meter or by means of the switch, S1, which then is read by the VTVM. Change the switch position so that the voltage now being read by the VTVM is the output voltage of the amplifier. This is done by placing the probe across the transistor in the last stage of the amplifier. This reading is then compared to the first. Because the input and output impedances of an amplifier are never the same, calculating the power gain by measuring the input and output voltages must involve a correction factor to resolve the impedance difference. To avoid this, we will work with input power and output power. The most convenient formula to obtain power from voltage for this is:

$$P = \frac{E^2}{R}$$

So if we had 0.1 volts into an amplifier having a 50,000 ohms input impedance, the power input would be:

$$P_i = \frac{0.1^2}{50,000} = 0.0000002 \text{ watts, or}$$

$$2 \times 10^{-7} \text{ watts}$$

If this input power produced an output power of 15 watts, the power gain of the amplifier in dB would be:

$$dB = 10 \log \frac{P_o}{P_i}$$

$$= 10 \log \frac{15}{2 \times 10^{-7}}$$

$$= 10 \log 7.5 \times 10^7 \text{, or } 10 \times 7.87$$
$$= 78.7 \text{ dB}$$

Where: dB = power gain in dB
   $P_o$ = input power
   $P_i$ = output power

The test should be repeated at several frequencies.

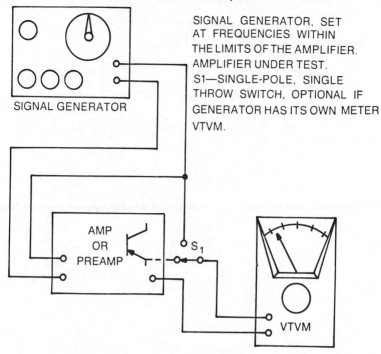

SIGNAL GENERATOR, SET
AT FREQUENCIES WITHIN
THE LIMITS OF THE AMPLIFIER.
AMPLIFIER UNDER TEST.
S1—SINGLE-POLE, SINGLE
THROW SWITCH, OPTIONAL IF
GENERATOR HAS ITS OWN METER
VTVM.

## MEASURING HUM AND NOISE

Noise is any unwanted signal which is caused by a variety of sources: improperly functioning tubes or transistors, even a dirty volume control will introduce noise. Hum, on the other hand, usually consists of the line frequency, 60 Hz in this country, and 50 Hz in Europe, which makes its way into the amplifier through the power supply. Another source of hum is the second harmonic of the line frequency, which would be 100 or 120 Hz, depending on where you live. An improperly dressed power line running close to some component in a high gain stage will cause hum. The cure is to move that line around until the hum disappears. The transformer may not be shielded sufficiently and the line frequency leaks into the amplifying stages.

### Procedure

Connect the signal generator to the amplifier or preamp as shown. The signal generator frequency is then set for the type of amplifier you are testing, RF or AF. If RF is used, then the probes should be also RF. Turn up the tone controls, both bass

**Measuring hum and noise**

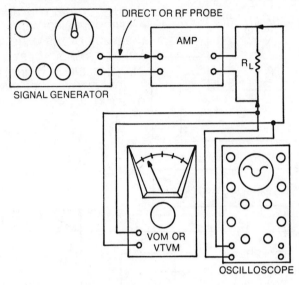

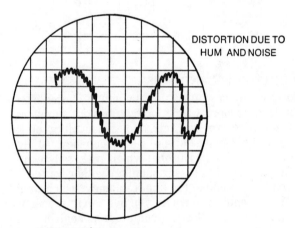

DISTORTION DUE TO
HUM AND NOISE

EQUIPMENT
SIGNAL GENERATOR.
AMPLIFIER BEING TESTED.
$R_L$—LOAD RESISTOR FOR EACH OPEN JACK.
VOM OR VTVM.
OSCILLOSCOPE, SET TO READ LINE FREQUENCY.

and treble, to their maximum position. Do the same for the volume control. We want to hear the worst possible case. Make sure a dummy load is connected across the terminals of the amplifier. If any output jacks are open, a resistor should be connected across each set of terminals. An open jack is a great source of hum. Connect the set of probes from the VTVM and the oscilloscope to the amplifier's output with its load. Note the voltage reading on the meter of the VTVM or VOM. This is the combined signal with hum and noise. Set the scope to read the frequency band from 60 to 120 Hz. The noise will appear as "hash," as it's called. The level of hum should be at least 60 dB below that of the full output of the amplifier. While the units are connected together, see if changing lead dressing gives better readings. Try a piece of tinfoil around the transformer to see if the hum is reduced. Be careful as you are doing that so the foil does not cause any shorts.

## VOLTAGE DIVIDER TO TEST PREAMP

Some generators are undependable when operating in the low voltage ranges. Then there are times, when testing a preamp, that the output of the generator may be way, way down. If there is any doubt in your mind as to the functioning of the low output of your generator, the set up shown below avoids any possibility of error since you are using a higher voltage scale which has a tendency to be generally more accurate.

### Procedure

The VTVM is connected across the output of the generator which is set in the middle frequencies. It is not important which frequencies are being employed to make the test. The equation below helps calculate the voltage actually applied to the preamp. The circuit can be made up permanently with precision resistors.

$$V2 = V1 \times \frac{R2}{R1 + R2}$$

where: V1 is the voltage measured by the meter
V2 is the voltage applied to the preamp.

R1 and R2 should be chosen to provide an easily calculable factor, such as one resistor being 9 times that of the other. The load resistor, R1, should be equal to the input impedance of the unit commonly attached to the output of the preamp.

**Voltage divider to check generator output**

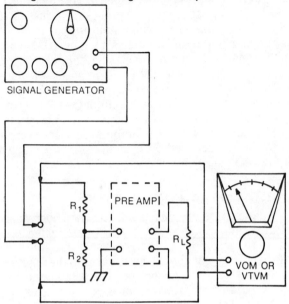

EQUIPMENT
AUDIO SIGNAL GENERATOR, SET AT SOME LOW OUTPUT RANGE.
VTVM, SET TO READ LOW VOLTAGES.
R1 AND R2 ARE CHOSEN TO PROVIDE AN EASILY CALCULABLE
FACTOR WHEN SUBSTITING V1 IN THE EQUATION IN THE TEXT.
$R_L$ IS CHOSEN TO BE EQUAL TO THE INPUT IMPEDANCE OF THE
UNITS MOST COMMONLY CONNECTED TO THE OUTPUT OF THE PRE-
AMP, IN THIS CASE THAT OF THE VTVM.

## DIFFERENTIATING FOR LOW DISTORTION MEASUREMENTS

It is a common fault to believe that the eye can recognize three percent, or even one percent, distortion with a sine wave. It is also true that, even with a square wave, the modern amplifiers with their tiny percentage of distortion become difficult to measure accurately. However, a triangle wave generator offers an excellent way of testing a low distortion amplifier with quite accurate results. Add a differentiator to the triangle wave and the distortion which is not visible

## Differentiating for low distortion measurements

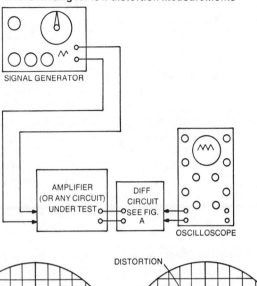

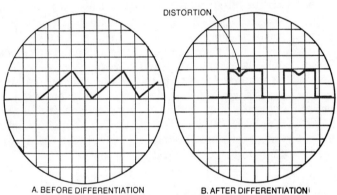

A. BEFORE DIFFERENTIATION

B. AFTER DIFFERENTIATION

DISTORTION

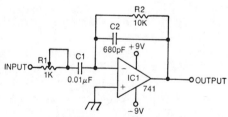

DIFFERENTIATING CIRCUIT

B1—9-VOLT BATTERY
C1—0.01 μF PAPER TUBULAR CAPACITOR
C2—680 pF DISC CERAMIC CAPACITOR
IC1—741 OP AMP (RADIO SHACK 276—010, OR EQUAL)
R1—1000 OHM LINEAR TAPER POT
R2—10000 OHM CARBON RESISTOR

ordinarily cannot only be seen, but the percentage of distortion can be estimated.

## Procedure

The triangle wave generator is connected to the input of the amplifier under test. The amplifier in turn is connected to the differentiating circuit, shown in the illustration. The oscilloscope presents the result from the output of the differentiating circuit. What this circuit does is convert the triangle wave with unrecognizable distortion to a square wave. But the square wave, because of the differentiating circuit, appears with a notch indicating distortion, if any. The depth of that notch is an indication of the degree of distortion. Its position shows at what amplitude the distortion exists. See scope pictures A and B for the before-and-after traces of differentiation.

## CHECKING ROOM FOR SPEAKER PLACEMENT

This test is suggested when determining just where a speaker or speakers would sound best. This test is a simplified version of what sound reinforcement specialists call "drawing a sound profile of a room." It avoids hanging or placing a speaker, then running wires to it only to find that when all the work is done, the speaker doesn't sound well. This test will discover dead spots and annoying reverberations. It will also indicate to a degree if the walls need tapestry hangings, or if there is too much overstuffed furniture present to satisfy the ears of the demanding audio purist.

## Procedure

Connect the speakers to the amplifier with enough wire so the speakers can be moved around. Connect the signal generator to the amplifier and feed it an audio tone. Connect a microphone to a small amplifier which has little distortion. Terminate the microphone's amplifier with a load resistor equal to the impedance of the speaker and across that load connect the inputs to the scope. Turn all of the amplifiers on and move the microphone to where you expect to sit. The speakers are placed where you believe they should go. An audio sweep generator is best for this test, since it shows the results over a wide sweep of frequencies at one time. Without it you can get along, but it means varying the frequency output of the generator manually as you (or an assistant) watch the traces on the scope.

The trace on the scope will be composed of the original tone plus some distortion in both amps, and the reverberations

**Checking room for speaker placement**

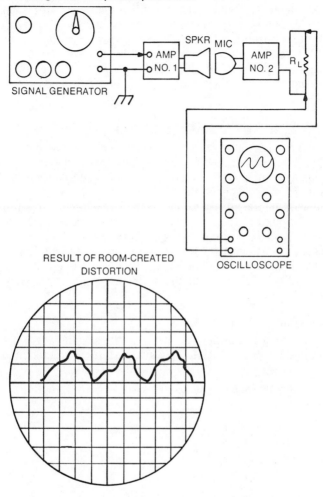

RESULT OF ROOM-CREATED
DISTORTION

EQUIPMENT
AUDIO SIGNAL GENERATOR OR SWEEP GENERATOR
AMPLIFIER NO. 1, USED TO DRIVE SPEAKER
AMPLIFIER No. 2, FOR MICROPHONE AMPLIFICATION
MICROPHONE—ANY TYPE WILL DO, AS LONG AS IT IS ABLE
TO
COVER THE FREQUENCIES OF INTEREST
OSCILLOSCOPE
$R_L$—A RESISTOR WHOSE RESISTANCE IS EQUAL IN VALUE
TO
THE SPEAKER NORMALLY CONNECTED TO THE OUTPUT

from the walls plus some distortion introduced by the microphone. Dead spots will show up—for certain frequencies—on the scope as distorted traces. By moving the furniture around, you may be able to remove the dead spots and introduce more reverberation if the room is too "dead." Are the speakers in a position where both high and low frequencies are heard? Can they be moved around for a better effect?

## CHECKING FOR SPEAKER RATTLES

Speakers develop rattles which, even if in themselves are minor, become annoying when it interferes with one's listening pleasure. Such rattles may be a tiny piece of wood pulling away from a corner of the enclosure, a brace not rigid against the wall, or the speaker cone itself. When too much power has been applied to them, speaker cones have been known to rip. What is less serious is the bolts which hold down the speakers—after a time they may vibrate loose so the rim of the speaker moves back and forth. Whatever the cause, a signal generator can help you discover just what is causing that annoying rattle.

### Procedure

Connect the audio generator to the speaker terminals, or in the case of a multiple speaker system, to the terminals in

**Checking speaker rattles**

SIGNAL GENERATOR

SPEAKER
ENCLOSURE

back of the enclosure. Remove the front or the back of the enclosure so you can see the speakers. Begin with a low frequency and a low output voltage. Slowly go up the scale until the rattle is heard. Keeping the generator set at that frequency, check each speaker in turn. Press against any suspect braces and tighten the bolts that may have worked loose. If a rip is seen in the speaker cone, you are out of luck. Some rips may be repaired with a drop of one of the many plastic glues on the market. In most cases, the speaker is irrepairable and is best thrown away.

If you have been able to stop the rattle, go up and down the scale with the generator once more as a check before you seal the enclosure.

## MEASURING SPEAKER IMPEDANCE

Although the impedance of a speaker may be specified, it is for one frequency only. Then too, the total impedance of a combination of speakers usually remains a mystery. The setup described here allows you to determine the complete impedance of not only one speaker, but of a group of speakers.

### Procedure

The output of an audio signal generator is connected to the speaker across a potentiometer. The principle is that when the resistance of the pot is equal to the speaker at some chosen frequency, we can obtain the impedance of the speaker at that frequency. Tune the generator to 400 Hz with the output level set at one volt. The potentiometer, R1, is adjusted until the voltage across the pot is the same as the voltage across the speaker leads. The probes of the AC VTVM are then moved as shown. Once that has been achieved, the resistance of the pot at that point is measured. The active part of the resistance as measured is equal to the impedance of the speaker. Now choose a series of other frequencies and measure the resistance of the pot for each point you choose, just as you did for the 400 Hz point. With enough points plotted on a graph marked as in the illustration, (impedance versus frequency) you can obtain a complete picture of the impedance curve of the speaker, or speakers. Since the enclosure affects the impedance, (mechanically loads the speaker) the curve will have particular meaning when the behavior of the enclosure is checked. It also allows making a comparison between one enclosure and another.

**Measuring speaker impedance**

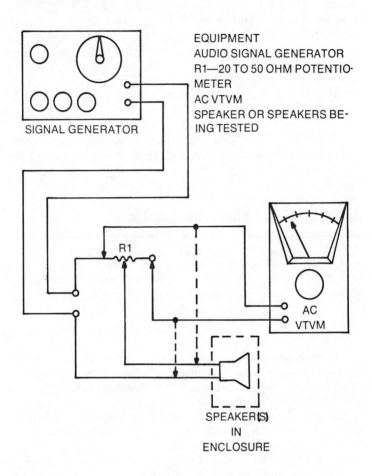

EQUIPMENT
AUDIO SIGNAL GENERATOR
R1—20 TO 50 OHM POTENTIO-
METER
AC VTVM
SPEAKER OR SPEAKERS BE-
ING TESTED

SIGNAL GENERATOR

R1

AC
VTVM

SPEAKER(S)
IN
ENCLOSURE

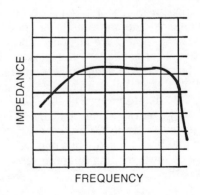

IMPEDANCE

FREQUENCY

## MEASURING SPEAKER RESONANCE

This test permits measuring the resonance of a speaker. Knowing this measurement, you can determine the "rightness" of an enclosure for the speaker—and also to allow matching a speaker to an amplifier. When a manufacturer sells an amplifier and a speaker to go with it, he has made sure that the speaker matches the amplifier. But, if you bought the amplifier and then, done as most of us do, buy speakers later or add others, we are never certain that they match. The test can be performed with the speaker in an enclosure or in free air. By doing both separately, you can find out if the enclosure adds or detracts from the speaker's resonance point.

**Measuring speaker resonance**

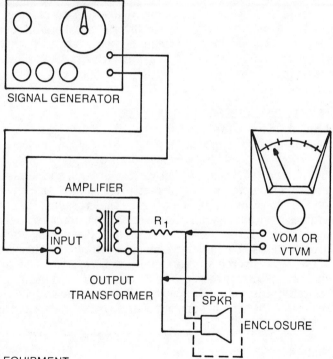

EQUIPMENT
SIGNAL GENERATOR
AMPLIFIER WHICH WILL BE USED WITH THE SPEAKER
SPEAKER/S
R1—AT LEAST TEN TIMES THE VALUE OF THE SPEAKER'S SPECIFIED IMPEDANCE
VOM OR VTVM

## Procedure

The audio signal generator's outputs are connected to the inputs of the amplifier. The output voltage should be enough to drive the amplifier to about half rated output. Set the frequency at the lowest point at which the amplifier is capable of handling. The VTVM connected across the output of the amplifier is set at a range low enough so that it will encompass the varying voltage levels that are expected. Now, tune the generator frequency upward slowly. As you go up, there will be a sharp deflection in the meter at some point. As you continue going up the frequency range, other peaks will show on the meter. The highest peak of all is the natural resonance of the speaker, or of the speaker within its enclosure. If you wish, you can draw a graph, plotting AC voltage versus frequency. This will give you an overall indication of the behavior of the speaker. This knowledge can be of value, especially if you plan to place several speakers in one enclosure and you want to make certain there is enough overlapping on the part of the speakers so that no "holes" will appear in the music.

## DETERMINING CROSSOVER POINTS FOR SPEAKER NETWORK

The audiophile who has built his own speaker enclosure and put in several speakers is now faced with the problem of putting in a crossover circuit between each set of speakers. If the crossover points are not correctly determined, there will either be too much lapover with the resultant sound "muddiness" or not enough crossover so there are holes in the musical scale. Either effect is bad and the arrangement illustrated shows how to determine each point for the speaker network. This scheme works equally well regardless of the number of speakers involved. The principle is to find the upper and lower limits for each speaker, then drop down 3 dB to make certain there is just enough overlap between the various ranges.

## Procedure

First feed the lowest tone capable of being reproduced by the woofer to the speaker by means of a direct probe. The generator should be set at an output voltage which can be read by the VTVM on its AC voltage scale. Then sweep the generator upward. At the upper limit of the woofer, there will be a sharp deflection noted on the meter needle. This is limit of that speaker. Back down 3 dB. This voltage level should be

**Determining crossover points for speaker network**

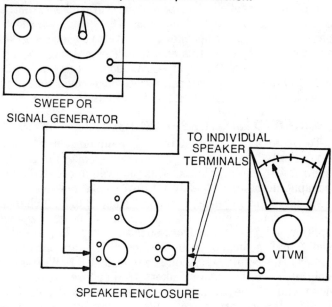

SWEEP OR
SIGNAL GENERATOR

TO INDIVIDUAL
SPEAKER
TERMINALS

VTVM

SPEAKER ENCLOSURE

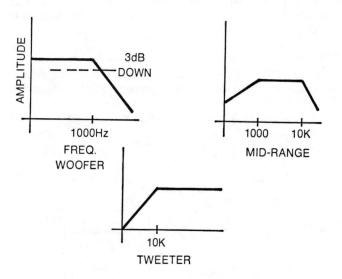

3dB
DOWN

1000Hz

FREQ.
WOOFER

MID-RANGE

1000    10K

TWEETER

10K

EQUIPMENT
SWEEP OR AUDIO SIGNAL GENERATOR
SPEAKERS BEING TESTED
VTVM

written down for reference. Find the lower and upper limits of the mid-range speaker. Then back down 3 dB and note that. Do the same for the remaining speakers. The illustration shows a typical curve for three speakers. However, your own speakers may vary greatly from this example. The crossover network is now built to cover these crossover points. For information on how to build a crossover filter, books that cover the subject of speaker enclosure building should be consulted.

## CHECKING PHASING OF SPEAKERS

To avoid bass loss and that "hole-in-the-center" sound, which results in a ping-pong effect, two speakers in a stereo system must be in phase. This is even more true in a quadraphonic setup. An easy way of making certain that all the speakers are in phase is to apply a signal to both channels of the stereo amplifier. In the case of a quadraphonic amplifier, let's take the front speakers first. The amplified audio signal is picked up by a microphone in front of each speaker. The results are then seen on the CRT. With a quad amplifier, once the front speakers are in phase (as described below) one of the front speakers and one of the back are matched. If they are out of phase, *only* the back speaker's connections are reversed. Then the fourth speaker is matched to the third.

### Procedure

Use the setup as shown. Make sure each microphone is the same distance from its respective speaker. Also ensure that

Checking phasing of speakers

SIGNAL GENERATOR

STEREO AMPLIFIER SPKRS

LFT

RT

MICROPHONES OSCILLOSCOPE

214

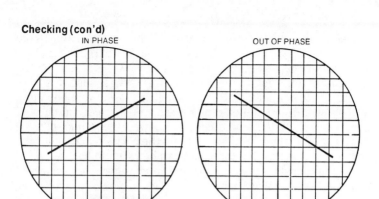

EQUIPMENT
AUDIO SIGNAL GENERATOR
AUDIO AMPLIFIER
TWO SPEAKERS (OR 4 SPEAKERS IN THE CASE OF QUADRAPHONIC)
M1, M2—TWO INEXPENSIVE CRYSTAL MICROPHONES
OSCILLOSCOPE

each channel of the amplifier is set at the same volume. Use a low-frequency signal of about 400 Hz. With the scope's controls adjusted properly, you should obtain a diagonal straight line on the CRT. The difference between in-phase and out-of-phase is that, with the first, the line will slant from lower left to upper right and in the latter, from lower right to upper left.

Now remove one of the front speakers and substitute one of the rear speakers. Reverse the leads of the rear speaker if need be. Then do the same for the fourth speaker.

## MEASURING FREE AIR RESONANCE OF A WOOFER

An enclosure is more than just a box to hold one or more speakers. Even if the box is airtight, this does not mean that the speaker will sound as well as it should. This is of particular importance when designing an enclosure which will contain a woofer. It is that speaker that determines the total volume of the enclosure and so for that reason the resonance frequency must be found.

### Procedure

The output of the signal generator is connected across the speaker leads through R1, which should be at least ten times the rated impedance of the woofer being tested. The VOM or VTVM is also connected across the speaker leads. The woofer should be suspended on wires so that it does not rest on any surface with which it might vibrate. Tune the generator to the lowest frequency the woofer is capable of reproducing. Now tune the generator frequency upwards while watching the VTVM. At one point, the VTVM will show a sudden surge. There will be other points reflecting this effect, but one point will show a much higher reading. This is the resonant point of the woofer. With this quantity known, the value can be substituted in the formulas to obtain the correct volume for the enclosure. The needed formulas can be found in books dealing with the construction of speaker enclosures. An incorrect volume will severly handicap the best speakers, while the enclosure that is well designed will greatly enhance even an ordinary speaker.

**Measuring free air resonance of a woofer**

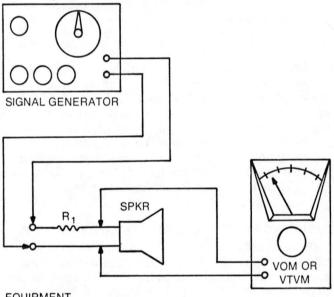

EQUIPMENT
SIGNAL GENERATOR
R1—RESISTOR AT LEAST TEN TIMES THE SPECIFIED
IMPEDANCE OF THE
SPEAKER UNDER TEST
SPEAKER BEING TESTED
VOM OR VTVM

# Chapter 8

# Checking Tape Recorders

Tape recorders, once considered almost luxury items, are now very readily found in almost every home and in more and more automobiles. Therefore, it would behoove one to be able to perform easy tests to verify proper operation and performance of a tape machine. Using a signal generator, as outlined in this chapter, will help you do that task.

## CHOOSING THE RIGHT TAPE FOR A RECORDER

Many tape recorders do not have an adjustable bias, so you should find the best tape for the particular machine being used. In all cases, a manufacturer recommends a specific brand of tape for his machine, since he wants you to get the maximum from his product. But, there may be alternate brands which will do just as well. Sometimes there are great buys in tapes, but without knowing which is suitable for your machine, you may make many poor recordings. The type tape can make a big difference in the end result. When you find the best tape for your machine by the method suggested below, you can continue using it with assurance that each recording will be as good as your machine can produce.

### Procedure

First, buy a small quantity of several brands of tape you would like to experiment with. Follow the setup as shown in the illustration. The signal generator's output is fed to the line or microphone input of the recorder. Adjust the output voltage of the generator to provide full output from the recorder. Record several minutes of a tone of about 400 Hz. Set the recording level so that a zero VU reading is obtained on the machine's meter or on the VTVM. A VOM can also be used if it has a dB scale. After several minutes of recording continuous tone, play the tape back. The tape should now offer the same reading—zero VU. If the tape is not right for your machine there will be a noticeable variance in the readings. This arrangement allows you to determine if the tape is of poor quality or has "dropouts," which will cause sharp deflections on the meter on playback. This is caused by the oxide coating particles not adhering properly to the plastic base tape itself. Where the oxide particles are missing, there is no recording.

**Choosing correct tape for recorder**

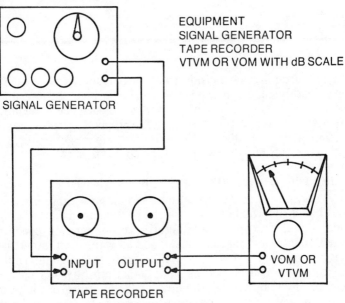

EQUIPMENT
SIGNAL GENERATOR
TAPE RECORDER
VTVM OR VOM WITH dB SCALE

SIGNAL GENERATOR

INPUT    OUTPUT

VOM OR
VTVM

TAPE RECORDER

## SETTING CORRECT BIAS FOR TAPE RECORDER

The better tape recorders have bias circuits which can be adjusted either by means of a potentiometer or a variable capacitor. Regardless of which component is employed, the principle remains the same. The best setting of the bias level will give the highest signal-to-noise ratio. But, care must be taken when trying to achieve this. Decreasing the bias will improve the high frequency output, but this will be at the cost of increased distortion and a lower signal output. The best bias setting is one in which a compromise is reached so that no one factor is obtained at the cost of the other two  An audio generator allows setting the best bias setting for your particular recorder.

**Procedure**

The output of the sine wave generator is connected to the input of the tape recorder. This can be the line input of the machine or the microphone input. The voltage output of the generator should be set so that it matches the output level of a microphone or a radio receiver, etc., depending on which input has been chosen. A low frequency wave is chosen—usually 400 Hz—while the recorder is in the recording mode. As the tape is running, the bias is adjusted so that the meter on the VTVM reads a value slightly higher than the value which produces a maximum output level of the signal when the machine is in the replay mode. It is a matter of a trial and error with a two-head machine, since immediate monitoring cannot be done with such an arrangement.

A three-head machine permits switching the VU meter on the machine from Record to Replay (on many units). If this is not possible, an AC VTVM can be used to read the level—either in conjunction with the VU meter, or in place of it. AC VTVMs have their meters marked in dBs as well as voltage and they

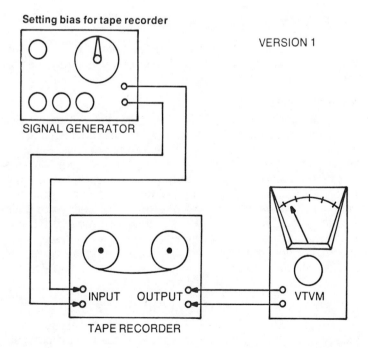

**Setting bias for tape recorder**

VERSION 1

SIGNAL GENERATOR

INPUT  OUTPUT  VTVM

TAPE RECORDER

**Setting bias for tape recorder**

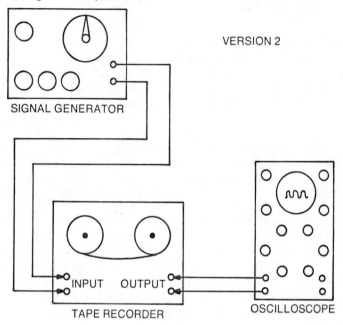

VERSION 2

SIGNAL GENERATOR

INPUT    OUTPUT

TAPE RECORDER          OSCILLOSCOPE

are usually more dependable than the VU meter on the recorder.

The test should be repeated with the generator being set at 1000 Hz and then at 10 kHz. All three tones should provide the same output value for the same tape.

### Alternate Version

With a three-head machine which has an A-B switch, the signal can be compared between that which is injected into the machine and that which the tape is reproducing. For this setup, see Version 2. An oscilloscope is plugged into the monitor jack, or into the output jack, depending on the machine. As the tone is being recorded, the bias is adjusted very slowly while the A-B switch is flipped back and forth. This should be continued until there is no appreciable difference between one position of the switch or the other. The scope has the further advantage of showing if distortion exists at certain settings of the bias control. Either version will improve the quality of the recordings to a dramatic level.

### DETERMINING CORRECT RECORDING LEVEL

To get the best possible tape recordings—those made yourself—the music must be recorded at the highest possible

**Determining correct recording level**

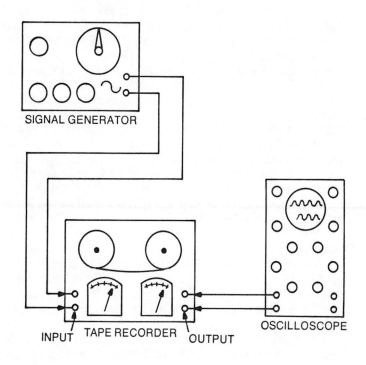

INPUT    TAPE RECORDER    OUTPUT     OSCILLOSCOPE

SIGNAL GENERATOR

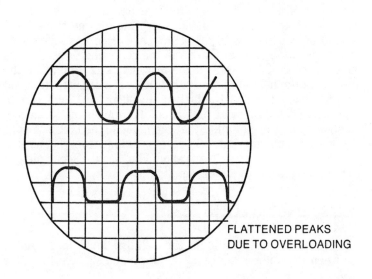

FLATTENED PEAKS
DUE TO OVERLOADING

level *before saturation* sets in. When the recording level has been set too high, the distortion becomes very apparent. To avoid this, one must record just below that saturation point. How to arrive at this? The VU meter on the machine has a red band which tells you that if the recording is set too high, distortion will occur. However, unless your machine is of broadcast quality, the meter will be of not much value, except as a rough check. A signal generator producing a continuous tone will easily tell you at what level your gain should be. A continuous sine wave can be recorded at a higher level than is otherwise permissible—even with music containing high dynamic peaks. To use the signal generator correctly as a means of running a level check, the characteristics of the VU meter must be taken into consideration. To achieve this, the arrangement shown in the illustration is suggested.

**Procedure**

The signal generator is connected to the input of the tape recorder. If you are using the line input, then the output voltage will be in the neighborhood of 250 mV; in the microphone inputs, 0.25 mV (or above) would be about right. The frequency for the first test should be approximately 400 Hz. The output of the recorder goes to the vertical inputs of the scope. Put the machine in the recording mode and run the tape for several minutes as you adjust the output voltage of the generator. The gain control setting on the recorder should be at about the halfway point. The output voltage should give you a reading of +3 dB. Now stop the tape and reset the generator so that the tone is at 5000 Hz. This time the reference level should be set to read 20 dB below *peak recording level*. This will avoid tape saturation due to the recording pre-emphasis characteristics. Now repeat the test at 10 kHz. Play back the tape form the beginning and see if there is a consistently good recording level and particularly if any distortion is apparent to the ears. Should there be distortion, that means that your gain control cannot be set quite that high, due to the fact that your VU meter is not accurate. But, that is unimportant just as long as you know what your levels should be. See the scope picture for clipping due to overloading.

**MEASURING SIGNAL TO NOISE
RATIO OF TAPE RECORDER**

Signal to noise ratio is the relative level in playback between the audio signal and the unwanted signals. In a tape recorder, these unwanted signals consist of tape hiss, motor rumble, and hum picked up by the playback and recording electronics. This relative level is expressed in dB.

There are divergent figures for S/N ratio for tape recorders—even of the same quality. This is due to the manufacturers using a different base from which to calculate the ratio. In some cases, only 1% harmonic distortion is allowed while others allow 2 or even 3%. The National Association of Radio and Television Broadcasters (NARTB) standard is 2%, while 3% harmonic distortion has been admitted as the base for most home machines. So for your own

**Measuring signal to noise ratio**

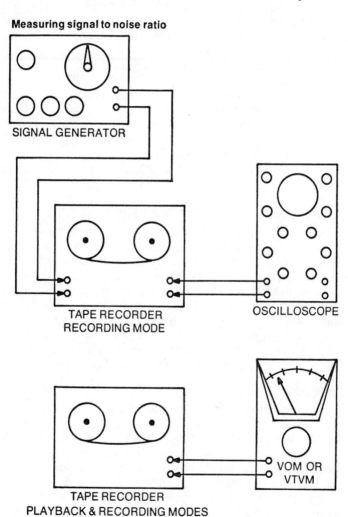

SIGNAL GENERATOR

TAPE RECORDER
RECORDING MODE

OSCILLOSCOPE

VOM OR
VTVM

TAPE RECORDER
PLAYBACK & RECORDING MODES

223

calculations, you may use the figure you prefer, or try all three to see the difference.

A high quality machine has VU meters calibrated to read zero VU when a recording at 400 Hz produces 1% distortion on the tape. But, this is true of only the very best machines. We would suggest a 2% figure for the first set of calculations.

### Procedure

Using the set-up shown, a 400 Hz tone is recorded from a sine wave generator. The machine is set to record at 7.5 ips, which is the standard speed. Slower speeds will always generate higher distortion. A distortion meter is best to record the amount of distortion, although a scope is more generally available. A dependable VU meter calibrated for 2% distortion can also be used. See the illustration for the arrangement and playback of the tape while measuring its output level. This can be read either by a VOM or VTVM with a dB scale. With a three-head machine, the output measurement can be done even while the tape is being recorded. With a two-head recorder, the tape must be run through once again, but with the machine in the recording mode with no input signal. The recorded result is noise only. This millivolt signal is made up only of noise—the unwanted signals. The ratio between the first and second levels is the signal to noise ratio.

### MEASURING DISTORTION IN A TAPE RECORDER

One of the important parameters of a tape recorder is the distortion inherent in the unit. Distortion exists even in the most expensive and best designed machines, but if the percentage of distortion is known, the machine output can at least be kept down to that figure. Occasionally, it is even possible to reduce the percentage below that of the manufacturer's specs. The only unusual item needed for the test is a band-pass filter. This can either be built or bought ready-made. To build it requires texts on the subject, since filter designs are beyond the scope of this book.

### Procedure

The principle involved is the measurement of the third harmonic—which is the distortion most apparent to the ear. The output of the signal generator is connected to the input of the tape recorder. Either line or microphone inputs may be used, provided the input voltage matches the input sensitivity. The frequency is 400 Hz. The output of the recorder goes to the band-pass filter, which can be bypassed by the switch, S1. When the circuit in position, all but the 1200 Hz tone is attenuated. Level readings are taken at the input to the filter by placing S1 in position 1. Then, the switch is moved to position 2, which gives you the filter output. The difference between the two readings is expressed in dB and this is converted to a percentage of distortion by reference to the appropriate nomograph or table. There is bound to be some insertion loss due to the action of the filter. One more point to be considered, to obtain significant values, the filter should have a rejection factor of 60 to 65 dB.

**Measuring distortion in a tape recorder**

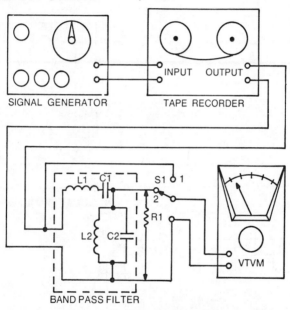

SIGNAL GENERATOR    TAPE RECORDER

BAND PASS FILTER

EQUIPMENT

AUDIO SIGNAL GENERATOR SET AT 400 Hz
TAPE RECORDER BEING CHECKED FOR DISTORTION
BAND-PASS FILTER MADE UP OF L1, L2 AND C1, C2 TO PASS
ONLY A 1200 Hz TONE WITH 60 TO 65 dB REJECTION
R1—PROPER TERMINATING RESISTOR FOR FILTER
VTVM, SET TO READ dB SCALE

## CHECKING TAPE HEAD AZIMUTH

It is of primary importance that tape record and playback heads be set physically exactly as they should be. If the horizontal adjustment (azimuth) is at odds with the tape as it is drawn past the heads, the playback response or the

225

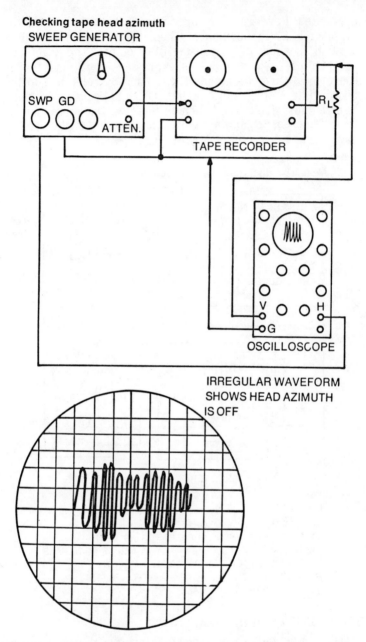

**Checking tape head azimuth**

SWEEP GENERATOR

SWP GD

ATTEN.

TAPE RECORDER

$R_L$

OSCILLOSCOPE

V   G   H

IRREGULAR WAVEFORM
SHOWS HEAD AZIMUTH
IS OFF

recording, depending on the function of the head, will suffer drastically. Although heads are placed in position correctly by the manufacturer—since he wants you to obtain the best possible results from your unit—vibration, general use, or an accidental blow will throw the head out of mechanical alignment. The result will be tapes that are not at all as they should sound. The azimuth alignment can be easily checked and can be corrected, if it is at fault, with the test results shown below.

**Procedure**

Hook the sweep generator to the input of the tape recorder. If the unit has its own amplifier, either connect the scope across the leads of the loudspeaker, or use a load resistor instead (with the ohmmage of the speaker) and capable of handling the power output of the amplifier. If the recorder has only a preamp, the oscilloscope vertical inputs can be connected across the output of the recorder. Put the recorder in the recording mode while sweeping the generator. With a three-head machine, the output can be checked directly by the scope. With two-head machines, where the recording head is used as the playback head, the process includes another step: Respool the tape and run it through again with the machine in the playback mode. If all is well the scope will show a smooth envelope on the waveform presentation. This envelope should extend from the lower to the upper limits of the recorder's frequency, as indicated by the manufacturer. But, if the waveform is irregular, as in the figure, then corrections must be made. Loosen the screws holding the tape head just enough so that the head can be wiggled slightly. With the eye, judge if the head is making smooth uniform contact with the tape. Now record again and check the results until you feel the head is positioned correctly. At the most, the re-positioning is slight. Once you are satisfied, bolt down the head so that it will not easily go out of alignment again and ruin another test tape. With care, excellent results are obtained with this procedure.

# Index

# Index

233